ALEKS Math in 30 Days!

The Most Effective ALEKS Math Crash Course

By

Reza Nazari

All inquiries should be addressed to:

info@EffortlessMath.com

www.EffortlessMath.com

ISBN: 978-1-63719-069-2

Published by: **Effortless Math Education Inc.**

For Online Math Practice Visit www.EffortlessMath.com

Welcome to
ALEKS Math Prep
2021

Thank you for choosing Effortless Math for your ALEKS Math test preparation and congratulations on making the decision to take the ALEKS test! It's a remarkable move you are taking, one that shouldn't be diminished in any capacity. That's why you need to use every tool possible to ensure you succeed on the test with the highest possible score, and this extensive study guide is one such tool.

If math has never been a strong subject for you, don't worry! This book will help you prepare for (and even ACE) the ALEKS Math assessment. As test day draws nearer, effective preparation becomes increasingly more important. Thankfully, you have this comprehensive study guide to help you get ready for the test. With this guide, you can feel confident that you will be more than ready for the ALEKS Math test when the time comes.

First and foremost, it is important to note that this book is a study guide and not a textbook. It is best read from cover to cover. Every lesson of this "self-guided math book" was carefully developed to ensure that you are making the most effective use of your time while preparing for the test. This up-to-date guide reflects the 2021 test guidelines and will put you on the right track to hone your math skills, overcome exam anxiety, and boost your confidence, so that you can have your best to succeed on the ALEKS Math test.

This study guide will:

- ☑ Explain the format of the ALEKS Math test.

- ☑ Describe specific test-taking strategies that you can use on the test.

- ☑ Provide ALEKS Math test-taking tips.

- ☑ Review all ALEKS Math concepts and topics you will be tested on.

- ☑ Help you identify the areas in which you need to concentrate your study time.

- ☑ Offer exercises that help you develop the basic math skills you will learn in each section.

- ☑ Give **2 realistic and full-length practice tests** (featuring new question types) with detailed answers to help you measure your exam readiness and build confidence.

This resource contains everything you will ever need to succeed on the ALEKS Math test. You'll get in-depth instructions on every math topic as well as tips and techniques on how to answer each question type. You'll also get plenty of practice questions to boost your test-taking confidence.

In addition, in the following pages you'll find:

➢ **How to Use This Book Effectively** – This section provides you with step-by-step instructions on how to get the most out of this comprehensive study guide.

➢ **How to study for the ALEKS Math Test** – A six-step study program has been developed to help you make the best use of this book and prepare for your ALEKS Math test. Here you'll find tips and strategies to guide your study program and help you understand ALEKS Math and how to ace the test.

➢ **ALEKS Math Review** – Learn everything you need to know about the ALEKS Math test.

➢ **ALEKS Math Test-Taking Strategies** – Learn how to effectively put these recommended test-taking techniques into use for improving your ALEKS Math score.

➢ **Test Day Tips** – Review these tips to make sure you will do your best when the big day comes.

Effortless Math's ALEKS Online Center

Effortless Math Online ALEKS Center offers a complete study program, including the following:

✓ Step-by-step instructions on how to prepare for the ALEKS Math test

✓ Numerous ALEKS Math worksheets to help you measure your math skills

✓ Complete list of ALEKS Math formulas

✓ Video lessons for all ALEKS Math topics

✓ Full-length ALEKS Math practice tests

✓ And much more…

No Registration Required.

Visit **EffortlessMath.com/ALEKS** to find your online ALEKS Math resources.

 www.EffortlessMath.com -- v

How to Use This Book Effectively

Look no further when you need a study guide to improve your math skills to succeed on the math portion of the ALEKS test. Each chapter of this comprehensive guide to the ALEKS Math will provide you with the knowledge, tools, and understanding needed for every topic covered on the test.

It's imperative that you understand each topic before moving onto another one, as that's the way to guarantee your success. Each chapter provides you with examples and a step-by-step guide of every concept to better understand the content that will be on the test. To get the best possible results from this book:

➢ **Begin studying long before your test date**. This provides you ample time to learn the different math concepts. The earlier you begin studying for the test, the sharper your skills will be. Do not procrastinate! Provide yourself with plenty of time to learn the concepts and feel comfortable that you understand them when your test date arrives.

➢ **Practice consistently**. Study ALEKS Math concepts at least 20 to 30 minutes a day. Remember, slow and steady wins the race, which can be applied to preparing for the ALEKS Math test. Instead of cramming to tackle everything at once, be patient and learn the math topics in short bursts.

➢ Whenever you get a math problem wrong, **mark it off, and review it later** to make sure you understand the concept.

➢ Start each session by looking over the previous related material.

➢ Once you've reviewed the book's lessons, **take a practice test** at the back of the book to gauge your level of readiness. Then, review your results. Read detailed answers and solutions for each question you missed.

➢ **Take another practice test** to get an idea of how ready you are to take the actual exam. Taking the practice tests will give you the confidence you need on test day. Simulate the ALEKS testing environment by sitting in a quiet room free from distraction. Make sure to clock yourself with a timer.

How to Study for the ALEKS Math Test

S tudying for the ALEKS Math test can be a really daunting and boring task. What's the best way to go about it? Is there a certain study method that works better than others? Well, studying for the ALEKS Math can be done effectively. The following six-step program has been designed to make preparing for the ALEKS Math test more efficient and less overwhelming.

Step 1 - Create a study plan
Step 2 - Choose your study resources
Step 3 - Review, Learn, Practice
Step 4 - Learn and practice test-taking strategies
Step 5 - Learn the ALEKS Test format and take practice tests
Step 6 - Analyze your performance

STEP 1: Create a Study Plan

It's always easier to get things done when you have a plan. Creating a study plan for the ALEKS Math test can help you to stay on track with your studies. It's important to sit down and prepare a study plan with what works with your life, work, and any other obligations you may have. Devote enough time each day to studying. It's also a great idea to break down each section of the exam into blocks and study one concept at a time.

It's important to understand that there is no "right" way to create a study plan. Your study plan will be personalized based on your specific needs and learning style.

Follow these guidelines to create an effective study plan for your ALEKS Math test:

★ **Analyze your learning style and study habits –** Everyone has a different learning style. It is essential to embrace your individuality and the unique way you learn. Think about what works and what doesn't work for you. Do you prefer ALEKS Math prep books or a combination of textbooks and video lessons? Does it work better for you if you study every night for thirty minutes or is it more effective to study in the morning before going to work?

★ **Evaluate your schedule** – Review your current schedule and find out how much time you can consistently devote to ALEKS Math study.

★ **Develop a schedule** – Now it's time to add your study schedule to your calendar like any other obligation. Schedule time for study, practice, and review. Plan out which topic you will study on which day to ensure that you're devoting enough time to each concept. Develop a study plan that is mindful, realistic, and flexible.

★ **Stick to your schedule** – A study plan is only effective when it is followed consistently. You should try to develop a study plan that you can follow for the length of your study program.

★ **Evaluate your study plan and adjust as needed** – Sometimes you need to adjust your plan when you have new commitments. Check in with yourself regularly to make sure that you're not falling behind in your study plan. Remember, the most important thing is sticking to your plan. Your study plan is all about helping you be more productive. If you find that your study plan is not as effective as you want, don't get discouraged. It's okay to make changes as you figure out what works best for you.

STEP 2: Choose Your Study Resources

There are numerous textbooks and online resources available for the ALEKS Math test, and it may not be clear where to begin. Don't worry! This study guide provides everything you need to fully prepare for your ALEKS Math test. In addition to the book content, you can also use Effortless Math's online resources. (video lessons, worksheets, formulas, etc.) On each page,  there is a link (and a QR code) to an online webpage which provides a comprehensive review of the topic, step-by-step instruction, video tutorial, and numerous examples and exercises to help you fully understand the concept.

Simply visit EffortlessMath.com/ALEKS to find your online ALEKS Math resources.

STEP 3: Review, Learn, Practice

This ALEKS Math study guide breaks down each subject into specific skills or content areas. For instance, the percent concept is separated into different topics–percent calculation, percent increase and decrease, percent problems, etc. Use this book to help you go over all key math concepts and topics on the ALEKS Math test.

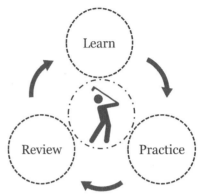

As you read each chapter, take notes or highlight the concepts you would like to go over again in the future. If you're unfamiliar with a topic or something is difficult for you, do additional research on it. For each math topic, plenty of instructions, step-by-step guides, and examples are provided to ensure you get a good grasp of the material. You can also find video lessons on the Effortless Math website for each ALEKS Math concept.

Quickly review the topics you do understand to get a brush-up of the material. Be sure to do the practice questions provided at the end of every chapter to measure your understanding of the concepts.

STEP 4: Learn and Practice Test-taking Strategies

This ALEKS Math study guide breaks down each subject into specific skills or content areas. For instance, the percent concept is separated into different topics–percent calculation, percent increase and decrease, percent problems, etc. Use this study guide and Effortless Math online ALEKS center to help you go over all key math concepts and topics on the ALEKS Math test.

STEP 5: Learn the ALEKS Test Format and Take Practice Tests

The *ALEKS Test Review* section provides information about the structure of the ALEKS test. Read this section to learn more about the ALEKS test structure, different test sections, the number of questions in each section, and the section time limits. When you have a prior understanding of the test format and different types of ALEKS Math questions, you'll feel more confident when you take the actual exam.

Once you have read through the instructions and lessons and feel like you are ready to go – take advantage of both of the full-length ALEKS Math practice tests available in this study guide. Use the practice tests to sharpen your skills and build confidence.

The ALEKS Math practice tests offered at the end of the book are formatted similarly to the actual ALEKS Math test. When you take each practice test, try to simulate actual testing conditions. To take the practice tests, sit in a quiet space, time yourself, and work through as many of the questions as time allows. The practice tests are followed by detailed answer explanations to help you find your weak areas, learn from your mistakes, and raise your ALEKS Math score.

STEP 6: Analyze Your Performance

After taking the practice tests, look over the answer keys and explanations to learn which questions you answered correctly and which you did not. Never be discouraged if you make a few mistakes. See them as a learning opportunity. This will highlight your strengths and weaknesses.

You can use the results to determine if you need additional practice or if you are ready to take the actual ALEKS Math test.

Looking for more?

Visit EffortlessMath.com/ALEKS to find hundreds of ALEKS Math worksheets, video tutorials, practice tests, ALEKS Math formulas, and much more.

Or scan this QR code.

No Registration Required.

ALEKS Test Review

ALEKS (Assessment and Learning in Knowledge Spaces) is an artificial intelligence-based assessment tool to measure the strengths and weaknesses of a student's mathematical knowledge. ALEKS is available for a variety of subjects and courses in K-12, Higher Education, and Continuing Education. The findings of ALEKS's assessment test help to find an appropriate level for course placement. The ALEKS math placement assessment ensures students' readiness for particular math courses at colleges.

ALEKS does not use multiple-choice questions like most other standardized tests. Instead, it utilizes adaptable and easy-to-use method that mimic paper and pencil techniques. When taking the ALEKS test, a brief tutorial helps you learn how to use ALEKS answer input tools. You then begin the ALEKS Assessment. In about 30 to 45 minutes, the test measures your current content knowledge by asking 20 to 30 questions. ALEKS is a Computer Adaptive (CA) assessment. It means that each question will be chosen on the basis of answers to all the previous questions. Therefore, each set of assessment questions is unique. The ALEKS Math assessment does not allow you to use a personal calculator. But for some questions ALEKS onscreen calculator button is active and the test taker can use it.

Key Features of the ALEKS Mathematics Assessment

Some key features of the ALEKS Math assessment are:

❖ Mathematics questions on ALEKS are adaptive to identify the student's knowledge from a comprehensive standard curriculum, ranging from basic arithmetic up to precalculus, including trigonometry but not calculus.

❖ Unlike other standardized tests, the ALEKS assessment does not provide a "grade" or "raw score." Instead, ALEKS identifies which concepts the student has mastered and what topics the student needs to learn.

❖ ALEKS does not use multiple-choice questions. Instead, students need to produce authentic mathematical input.

❖ There is no time limit for taking the ALEKS Math assessment. But it usually takes 30 to 45 minutes to complete the assessment.

The ALEKS Math score is between 1 and 100 and is interpreted as a percentage correct. A higher ALEKS score indicates that the test-taker has mastered more math concepts. ALEKS Math assessment tool evaluates mastery of a comprehensive set of mathematics skills ranging from basic arithmetic up to precalculus, including trigonometry but not calculus. It will place students in classes up to Calculus.

ALEKS Math Test-Taking Strategies

Here are some test-taking strategies that you can use to maximize your performance and results on the ALEKS Math test.

#1: USE THIS APPROACH TO ANSWER EVERY ALEKS MATH QUESTION

- Review the question to identify keywords and important information.

- Translate the keywords into math operations so you can solve the problem.

- Review the answer choices. What are the differences between answer choices?

- Draw or label a diagram if needed.

- Try to find patterns.

- Find the right method to answer the question. Use straightforward math, plug in numbers, or test the answer choices (backsolving).

- Double-check your work.

#2: ANSWER EVERY ALEKS MATH QUESTION

Don't leave any fields empty! ALEKS is a Computer Adaptive (CA) assessment. Therefore, you cannot leave a question unanswered, and you cannot go back to previous questions.

Even if you're unable to work out a problem, strive to answer it. Take a guess if you have to. You will not lose points by getting an answer wrong, though you may gain a point by getting it correct!

#3: Ballpark

A ballpark answer is a rough approximation. When we become overwhelmed by calculations and figures, we end up making silly mistakes. A decimal that is moved by one unit can change an answer from right to wrong, regardless of the number of steps that you went through to get it. That's where ballparking can play a big part.

If you think you know what the correct answer may be (even if it's just a ballpark answer), you'll usually have the ability to estimate the range of possible answers and avoid simple mistakes.

#4: Plugging In Numbers

"Plugging in numbers" is a strategy that can be applied to a wide range of different math problems on the ALEKS Math test. This approach is typically used to simplify a challenging question so that it is more understandable. By using the strategy carefully, you can find the answer without too much trouble.

The concept is fairly straightforward–replace unknown variables in a problem with certain values. When selecting a number, consider the following:

- Choose a number that's basic (just not too basic). Generally, you should avoid choosing 1 (or even 0). A decent choice is 2.

- Try not to choose a number that is displayed in the problem.

- Make sure you keep your numbers different if you need to choose at least two of them.

- If your question contains fractions, then a potential right answer may involve either an LCD (least common denominator) or an LCD multiple.

- 100 is the number you should choose when you are dealing with problems involving percentages.

ALEKS Mathematics – Test Day Tips

After practicing and reviewing all the math concepts you've been taught, and taking some ALEKS mathematics practice tests, you'll be prepared for test day. Consider the following tips to be extra-ready come test time.

Before Your Test

What to do the night before:

■ **Relax!** One day before your test, study lightly or skip studying altogether. You shouldn't attempt to learn something new, either. There are plenty of reasons why studying the evening before a big test can work against you. Put it this way–a marathoner wouldn't go out for a sprint before the day of a big race. Mental marathoners–such as yourself–should not study for any more than one hour 24 hours before a ALEKS test. That's because your brain requires some rest to be at its best. The night before your exam, spend some time with family or friends, or read a book.

■ **Avoid bright screens** - You'll have to get some good shuteye the night before your test. Bright screens (such as the ones coming from your laptop, TV, or mobile device) should be avoided altogether. Staring at such a screen will keep your brain up, making it hard to drift asleep at a reasonable hour.

■ **Make sure your dinner is healthy** - The meal that you have for dinner should be nutritious. Be sure to drink plenty of water as well. Load up on your complex carbohydrates, much like a marathon runner would do. Pasta, rice, and potatoes are ideal options here, as are vegetables and protein sources.

■ **Get your bag ready for test day** – Prefer to take ALEKS in the Testing Office? The night prior to your test, pack your bag with your stationery, admissions pass, ID, and any other gear that you need. Keep the bag right by your front door. If you prefer to take the test at home, find a quite place without any distractions.

■ **Make plans to reach the testing site** – If you are taking the test at the testing office, ensure that you understand precisely how you will arrive at the site of the test. If parking is something you'll have to find first, plan for it. If you're dependent on public transit, then review the schedule. You should also make sure that the train/bus/subway/streetcar you use will be running. Find out about road closures as well. If a parent or friend is accompanying you, ensure that they understand what steps they have to take as well.

The Day of the Test

- **Get up reasonably early, but not too early.**

- **Have breakfast** - Breakfast improves your concentration, memory, and mood. As such, make sure the breakfast that you eat in the morning is healthy. The last thing you want to be is distracted by a grumbling tummy. If it's not your own stomach making those noises, another test taker close to you might be instead. Prevent discomfort or embarrassment by consuming a healthy breakfast. Bring a snack with you if you think you'll need it.

- **Follow your daily routine** - Do you watch TV in the morning while getting ready for the day? Don't break your usual habits on the day of the test. Likewise, if coffee isn't something you drink in the morning, then don't take up the habit hours before your test. Routine consistency lets you concentrate on the main objective–doing the best you can on your test.

- **Wear layers** - Dress yourself up in comfortable layers if you are taking the test at the testing site. You should be ready for any kind of internal temperature. If it gets too warm during the test, take a layer off.

- **Make your voice heard** - If something is off, speak to a proctor. If medical attention is needed or if you'll require anything, consult the proctor prior to the start of the test. Any doubts you have should be clarified. You should be entering the test site with a state of mind that is completely clear.

- **Have faith in yourself** - When you feel confident, you will be able to perform at your best. When you are waiting for the test to begin, envision yourself receiving an outstanding result. Try to see yourself as someone who knows all the answers, no matter what the questions are. A lot of athletes tend to use this technique–particularly before a big competition. Your expectations will be reflected by your performance.

During your test

- **Be calm and breathe deeply** - You need to relax before the test, and some deep breathing will go a long way to help you do that. Be confident and calm. You got this. Everybody feels a little stressed out just before an evaluation of any kind is set to begin. Learn some effective breathing exercises. Spend a minute meditating before the test starts. Filter out any negative thoughts you have. Exhibit confidence when having such thoughts.

- **Concentrate on the test** - Refrain from comparing yourself to anyone else. You shouldn't be distracted by the people near you or random noise. Concentrate exclusively on the test. If you find yourself irritated by surrounding noises, earplugs can be used to block sounds off close to you. Don't forget–the test is going to last an hour or more. Some of that time will be dedicated to brief sections. Concentrate on the specific section you are working on during a particular moment. Do not let your mind wander off to upcoming or previous questions.

- **Try to answer each question individually** - Focus only on the question you are working on. Use one of the test-taking strategies to solve the problem. If you aren't able to come up with an answer, don't get frustrated. Simply guess, then move onto the next question.

- **Don't forget to breathe!** Whenever you notice your mind wandering, your stress levels boosting, or frustration brewing, take a thirty-second break. Shut your eyes, drop your pencil, breathe deeply, and let your shoulders relax. You will end up being more productive when you allow yourself to relax for a moment.

After your test

- **Take it easy** - You will need to set some time aside to relax and decompress once the test has concluded. There is no need to stress yourself out about what you could've said, or what you may have done wrong. At this point, there's nothing you can do about it. Your energy and time would be better spent on something that will bring you happiness for the remainder of your day.

- **Redoing the test** - Did you succeed on the test? Congratulations! Your hard work paid off! Succeeding on this test means that you are now ready to take college level courses.

  If you didn't receive the result you expected, though, don't worry! The test can be retaken. In such cases, you will need to follow the retake policy. You also need to re-register to take the exam again.

Contents

DAY 1 Fractions

Math topics that you'll learn in this chapter:

1. Simplifying Fractions

2. Adding and Subtracting Fractions

3. Multiplying and Dividing Fractions

Simplifying Fractions

☆ A fraction contains two numbers separated by a bar between them. The bottom number, called the denominator, is the total number of equally divided portions in one whole. The top number, called the numerator, is how many portions you have. And the bar represents the operation of division.

☆ Simplifying a fraction means reducing it to the lowest terms. To simplify a fraction, evenly divide both the top and bottom of the fraction by $2, 3, 5, 7$, etc.

☆ Continue until you can't go any further.

Examples:

Example 1. Simplify $\frac{15}{35}$

Solution: To simplify $\frac{15}{35}$, find a number that both 15 and 35 are divisible by. Both are divisible by 5. Then: $\frac{15}{35} = \frac{15 \div 5}{35 \div 5} = \frac{3}{7}$

Example 2. Simplify $\frac{30}{120}$

Solution: To simplify $\frac{30}{120}$, find a number that both 30 and 120 are divisible by. Both are divisible by 10 and 3. Then: $\frac{30}{120} = \frac{30 \div 10}{120 \div 10} = \frac{3}{12}$, 3 and 12 are divisible by 3, then: $\frac{3}{12} = \frac{1}{4}$

Example 3. Simplify $\frac{36}{42}$

Solution: To simplify $\frac{36}{42}$, find a number that both 36 and 42 are divisible by. Both are divisible by 6, then: $\frac{36}{42} = \frac{36 \div 6}{42 \div 6} = \frac{6}{7}$

bit.ly/3nOGNko

Find more at

Adding and Subtracting Fractions

☆ For "like" fractions (fractions with the same denominator), add or subtract the numerators (top numbers) and write the answer over the common denominator (bottom numbers).

☆ Adding and Subtracting fractions with the same denominator:

$$\frac{a}{b} + \frac{c}{b} = \frac{a+c}{b} \qquad \frac{a}{b} - \frac{c}{b} = \frac{a-c}{b}$$

☆ Find equivalent fractions with the same denominator before you can add or subtract fractions with different denominators.

☆ Adding and Subtracting fractions with different denominators:

$$\frac{a}{b} + \frac{c}{d} = \frac{ad+bc}{bd} \qquad \frac{a}{b} - \frac{c}{d} = \frac{ad-bc}{bd}$$

Examples:

Example 1. Find the sum. $\frac{1}{4} + \frac{2}{3} =$

$$\frac{(1)(3)+(2)(4)}{(4)(3)\ 12} = \frac{11}{12}$$

Solution: These two fractions are "unlike" fractions. (they have different denominators). Use this formula: $\frac{a}{b} + \frac{c}{d} = \frac{ad+cb}{bd}$

Then: $\frac{1}{4} + \frac{2}{3} = \frac{(1)(3)+(2)(4)}{4 \times 3} = \frac{3+8}{12} = \frac{11}{12}$

$$\frac{(5)(5)-(2)(6)}{(6)(5)} = \frac{37}{30}$$
$$30$$

Example 2. Find the difference. $\frac{5}{6} - \frac{2}{5} =$

Solution: For "unlike" fractions, find equivalent fractions with the same denominator before you can add or subtract fractions with different denominators. Use this formula: $\frac{a}{b} - \frac{c}{d} = \frac{ad-bc}{bd}$

$\frac{5}{6} - \frac{2}{5} = \frac{(5)(5)-(2)(6)}{6 \times 5} = \frac{25-12}{30} = \frac{13}{30}$

Multiplying and Dividing Fractions

☆ Multiplying fractions: multiply the top numbers and multiply the bottom numbers. Simplify if necessary. $\frac{a}{b} \times \frac{c}{d} = \frac{a \times c}{b \times d}$

☆ Dividing fractions: Keep, Change, Flip

☆ Keep the first fraction, change the division sign to multiplication, and flip the numerator and denominator of the second fraction. Then, solve!

$$\frac{a}{b} \div \frac{c}{d} = \frac{a}{b} \times \frac{d}{c} = \frac{a \times d}{b \times c}$$

Examples:

Example 1. Multiply. $\frac{2}{5} \times \frac{1}{7} =$

Solution: Multiply the top numbers and multiply the bottom numbers.
$\frac{2}{5} \times \frac{1}{7} = \frac{2 \times 1}{5 \times 7} = \frac{2}{35}$.

Example 2. Solve. $\frac{3}{5} \div \frac{2}{3} =$

Solution: Keep the first fraction, change the division sign to multiplication, and flip the numerator and denominator of the second fraction.
Then: $\frac{3}{5} \div \frac{2}{3} = \frac{3}{5} \times \frac{3}{2} = \frac{3 \times 3}{5 \times 2} = \frac{9}{10}$

Example 3. Calculate. $\frac{5}{8} \times \frac{3}{4} =$

Solution: Multiply the top numbers and multiply the bottom numbers.
$\frac{5}{8} \times \frac{3}{4} = \frac{5 \times 3}{8 \times 4} = \frac{15}{32}$
Then: $\frac{2}{9} \div \frac{3}{8} = \frac{2}{9} \times \frac{8}{3} = \frac{2 \times 8}{9 \times 3} = \frac{16}{27}$

Day 1: Practices

✎ Simplify each fraction.

1) $\frac{3}{6} = \frac{1}{2}$

2) $\frac{8}{16} = \frac{2}{4}$

3) $\frac{10}{50} = \frac{1}{5}$

4) $\frac{14}{16} = \frac{7}{8}$

5) $\frac{15}{35} =$

6) $\frac{28}{42} =$

7) $\frac{64}{72} =$

8) $\frac{63}{108} =$

✎ Find the sum or difference.

9) $\frac{3}{5} + \frac{2}{5} =$

10) $\frac{4}{7} - \frac{2}{7} =$

11) $\frac{2}{4} + \frac{5}{12} =$

12) $\frac{18}{21} - \frac{5}{7} =$

13) $\frac{12}{45} - \frac{1}{9} =$

14) $\frac{25}{56} - \frac{3}{7} =$

15) $\frac{22}{48} - \frac{3}{8} =$

16) $\frac{18}{39} + \frac{1}{13} =$

✎ Find the products or quotients.

17) $\frac{2}{16} \div \frac{4}{3} =$ $\frac{2}{16} \cdot \frac{3}{4} = \frac{6}{64} = \frac{2}{32}$

18) $\frac{1}{5} \div \frac{8}{25} =$

19) $\frac{9}{14} \times \frac{5}{21} =$

20) $\frac{15}{32} \times \frac{6}{15} =$

21) $\frac{2}{21} \div \frac{4}{3} =$

22) $\frac{14}{5} \div \frac{28}{35} =$

23) $\frac{7}{16} \times \frac{5}{20} =$ 3

24) $\frac{21}{42} \times \frac{12}{15} =$

Day 1: Answers

1) $\frac{1}{2}$

2) $\frac{1}{2}$

3) $\frac{1}{5}$

4) $\frac{7}{8}$

5) $\frac{3}{7}$

6) $\frac{2}{3}$

7) $\frac{8}{9}$

8) $\frac{7}{12}$

9) $\frac{5}{5} = 1$

10) $\frac{2}{7}$

11) $\frac{11}{12}$

12) $\frac{1}{7}$

13) $\frac{7}{45}$

14) $\frac{1}{56}$

15) $\frac{1}{12}$

16) $\frac{7}{13}$

17) $\frac{3}{32}$

18) $\frac{5}{8}$

19) $\frac{15}{98}$

20) $\frac{3}{16}$

21) $\frac{1}{14}$

22) $\frac{7}{2} = 3\frac{1}{2}$

23) $\frac{7}{64}$

24) $\frac{2}{5}$

Effortless Math Education

DAY 2 Mixed Numbers

Math topics that you'll learn in this chapter:

1. Adding Mixed Numbers

2. Subtracting Mixed Numbers

3. Multiplying Mixed Numbers

4. Dividing Mixed Numbers

7

Adding Mixed Numbers

Use the following steps for adding mixed numbers:

☆ Add whole numbers of the mixed numbers.

☆ Add the fractions of the mixed numbers.

☆ Find the Least Common Denominator (LCD) if necessary.

☆ Add whole numbers and fractions.

☆ Write your answer in lowest terms.

Examples:

Example 1. Add mixed numbers. $1\frac{1}{3} + 2\frac{1}{2} =$

Solution: Let's rewriting our equation with parts separated, $1\frac{1}{3} + 2\frac{1}{2} = 1 + \frac{1}{3} + 2 + \frac{1}{2}$.
Now, add whole number parts: $1 + 2 = 3$
Add the fraction parts $\frac{1}{3} + \frac{1}{2}$. Rewrite to solve with the equivalent fractions.
$\frac{1}{3} + \frac{1}{2} = \frac{2}{6} + \frac{3}{6} = \frac{5}{6}$. Now, combine the whole and fraction parts: $3 + \frac{5}{6} = 3\frac{5}{6}$

Example 2. Find the sum. $2\frac{3}{4} + 3\frac{2}{5} =$

Solution: Rewriting our equation with parts separated, $2 + \frac{3}{4} + 3 + \frac{2}{5}$. Add the whole number parts:
$2 + 3 = 5$. Add the fraction parts: $\frac{3}{4} + \frac{2}{5} = \frac{15}{20} + \frac{8}{20} = \frac{23}{20}$
Convert the improper fraction into a mixed number: $\frac{23}{20} = 1\frac{3}{20}$.
Now, combine the whole and fraction parts: $5 + 1\frac{3}{20} = 6\frac{3}{20}$

Subtracting Mixed Numbers

Use these steps for subtracting mixed numbers.

☆ Convert mixed numbers into improper fractions. $a\frac{c}{b} = \frac{ab+c}{b}$

☆ Find equivalent fractions with the same denominator for unlike fractions. (fractions with different denominators)

☆ Subtract the second fraction from the first one. $\frac{a}{b} - \frac{c}{d} = \frac{ad-bc}{bd}$

☆ Write your answer in lowest terms.

☆ If the answer is an improper fraction, convert it into a mixed number.

Examples:

Example 1. Subtract. $2\frac{1}{4} - 1\frac{1}{5} =$

Solution: Convert mixed numbers into fractions: $2\frac{1}{4} = \frac{2\times4+1}{4} = \frac{9}{4}$ and $1\frac{1}{5} = \frac{1\times5+1}{5} = \frac{6}{5}$
These two fractions are "unlike" fractions. (they have different denominators).
Find equivalent fractions with the same denominator. Use this formula:
$\frac{a}{b} - \frac{c}{d} = \frac{ad-bc}{bd}$
$\frac{9}{4} - \frac{6}{5} = \frac{(9)(5)-(6)(4)}{4\times5} = \frac{45-24}{20} = \frac{21}{20}$

Example 2. Find the difference. $3\frac{5}{7} - 2\frac{3}{4} =$

Solution: Convert mixed numbers into fractions: $3\frac{5}{7} = \frac{3\times7+5}{7} = \frac{26}{7}$ and
$2\frac{3}{4} = \frac{2\times4+3}{4} = \frac{11}{4}$
Then: $3\frac{5}{7} - 2\frac{3}{4} = \frac{26}{7} - \frac{11}{4} = \frac{(26)(4)-(11)(7)}{7\times4} = \frac{104-77}{7\times4} = \frac{27}{28}$

Multiplying Mixed Numbers

Use the following steps for multiplying mixed numbers:

☆ Convert the mixed numbers into fractions. $a\frac{c}{b} = a + \frac{c}{b} = \frac{ab+c}{b}$

☆ Multiply fractions. $\frac{a}{b} \times \frac{c}{d} = \frac{a \times c}{b \times d}$

☆ Write your answer in lowest terms.

☆ If the answer is an improper fraction (numerator is bigger than denominator), convert it into a mixed number.

Examples:

Example 1. Multiply. $2\frac{2}{3} \times 3\frac{5}{6} =$

Solution: Converting mixed numbers into fractions, $2\frac{2}{3} \times 3\frac{5}{6} = \frac{8}{3} \times \frac{23}{6}$
Apply the fractions rule for multiplication: $\frac{8}{3} \times \frac{23}{6} = \frac{8 \times 23}{3 \times 6} = \frac{184}{18} = 10\frac{2}{9}$

Example 2. Multiply. $5\frac{2}{3} \times 2\frac{2}{5} =$

Solution: Convert mixed numbers into fractions, $5\frac{2}{3} = \frac{5 \times 3 + 2}{3} = \frac{17}{3}$ and $2\frac{2}{5} = \frac{2 \times 5 + 2}{5} = \frac{12}{5}$.
Apply the fractions rule for multiplication: $\frac{17}{3} \times \frac{12}{5} = \frac{17 \times 12}{3 \times 5} = \frac{204}{15} = \frac{68}{5}$
The answer is an improper fraction. Convert it into a mixed number. $\frac{68}{5} = 13\frac{3}{5}$

Example 3. Find the product. $4\frac{3}{4} \times 3\frac{3}{8} =$

Solution: Convert mixed numbers to fractions: $4\frac{3}{4} = \frac{19}{4}$ and $3\frac{3}{8} = \frac{27}{8}$. Multiply two

fractions:

$\frac{19}{4} \times \frac{27}{8} = \frac{19 \times 27}{4 \times 8} = \frac{513}{32} = 16\frac{1}{32}$

bit.ly/3aPy7XJ

Find more at

Dividing Mixed Numbers

Use the following steps for dividing mixed numbers:

☆ Convert the mixed numbers into fractions. $a\frac{c}{b} = a + \frac{c}{b} = \frac{ab+c}{b}$

☆ Divide fractions: Keep, Change, Flip: Keep the first fraction, change the division sign to multiplication, and flip the numerator and denominator of the second fraction. Then, solve! $\frac{a}{b} \div \frac{c}{d} = \frac{a}{b} \times \frac{d}{c} = \frac{a \times d}{b \times c}$

☆ Write your answer in lowest terms.

☆ If the answer is an improper fraction (numerator is bigger than denominator), convert it into a mixed number.

Examples:

Example 1. Solve. $3\frac{1}{2} \div 1\frac{1}{3} =$

Solution: Convert mixed numbers into fractions: $3\frac{1}{2} = \frac{3 \times 2 + 1}{2} = \frac{7}{2}$ and $1\frac{1}{3} = \frac{1 \times 3 + 1}{3} = \frac{4}{3}$

Keep, Change, Flip: $\frac{7}{2} \div \frac{4}{3} = \frac{7}{2} \times \frac{3}{4} = \frac{7 \times 3}{2 \times 4} = \frac{21}{8}$. The answer is an improper fraction. Convert it into a mixed number: $\frac{21}{8} = 2\frac{5}{8}$

Example 2. Solve. $3\frac{2}{5} \div 2\frac{3}{7} =$

Solution: Convert mixed numbers to fractions, then solve:

$3\frac{2}{5} \div 2\frac{3}{7} = \frac{17}{5} \div \frac{17}{7} = \frac{17}{5} \times \frac{7}{17} = \frac{17 \times 7}{5 \times 17} = \frac{119}{85} = \frac{7}{5} = 1\frac{2}{5}$

Example 3. Solve. $4\frac{4}{5} \div 2\frac{2}{3} =$

Solution: Converting mixed numbers to fractions: $4\frac{4}{5} \div 2\frac{2}{3} = \frac{24}{5} \div \frac{8}{3}$

Keep, Change, Flip: $\frac{24}{5} \div \frac{8}{3} = \frac{24}{5} \times \frac{3}{8} = \frac{24 \times 3}{5 \times 8} = \frac{72}{40} = \frac{9}{5} = 1\frac{4}{5}$

Day 2: Practices

✎ Find the sum.

1) $2\frac{1}{5} + 1\frac{2}{5} =$

2) $5\frac{1}{9} + 2\frac{7}{9} =$

3) $2\frac{3}{4} + 1\frac{1}{8} =$

4) $2\frac{2}{7} + 4\frac{1}{21} =$

5) $5\frac{3}{5} + 1\frac{4}{9} =$

6) $3\frac{3}{11} + 4\frac{6}{7} =$

✎ Find the difference.

7) $5\frac{1}{3} - 4\frac{2}{3} =$

8) $4\frac{7}{10} - 1\frac{3}{10} =$

9) $3\frac{1}{3} - 2\frac{2}{9} =$

10) $6\frac{1}{2} - 3\frac{1}{3} =$

11) $4\frac{3}{4} - 2\frac{1}{28} =$

12) $4\frac{2}{7} - 3\frac{1}{6} =$

✎ Find the products.

13) $1\frac{1}{2} \times 2\frac{3}{7} = \frac{3}{2} \cdot \frac{17}{7} = \frac{51}{14} = 3\frac{9}{14}$

14) $1\frac{3}{4} \times 1\frac{3}{5} =$

15) $4\frac{1}{2} \times 1\frac{5}{6} =$

16) $1\frac{2}{7} \times 3\frac{1}{5} =$

17) $2\frac{1}{5} \times 5\frac{1}{2} =$

18) $2\frac{1}{2} \times 4\frac{4}{5} =$

✎ Solve.

19) $1\frac{1}{3} \div 1\frac{2}{3} =$

20) $2\frac{1}{4} \div 1\frac{1}{2} = \frac{9}{4} \div \frac{3}{2} = \frac{9}{4} \cdot \frac{2}{3} = \frac{18}{12} = 1\frac{6}{12} = 1\frac{1}{2}$

21) $5\frac{1}{3} \div 3\frac{1}{2} =$

22) $3\frac{2}{7} \div 1\frac{1}{8} =$

Effortless Math Education

Day 2: Answers

1) $3\frac{3}{5}$

2) $7\frac{8}{9}$

3) $3\frac{7}{8}$

4) $6\frac{1}{3}$

5) $7\frac{2}{45}$

6) $8\frac{10}{77}$

7) $\frac{2}{3}$

8) $3\frac{2}{5}$

9) $1\frac{1}{9}$

10) $3\frac{1}{6}$

11) $2\frac{5}{7}$

12) $1\frac{5}{42}$

13) $3\frac{9}{14}$

14) $2\frac{4}{5}$

15) $8\frac{1}{4}$

16) $4\frac{4}{35}$

17) $12\frac{1}{10}$

18) 12

19) $\frac{4}{5}$

20) $1\frac{1}{2}$

21) $1\frac{11}{21}$

22) $2\frac{58}{63}$

Effortless Math Education

DAY 3 Decimals

Math topics that you'll learn in this chapter:

1. Comparing Decimals
2. Rounding Decimals
3. Adding and Subtracting Decimals
4. Multiplying and Dividing Decimals

15

Comparing Decimals

☆ A decimal is a fraction written in a special form. For example, instead of writing $\frac{1}{2}$ you can write: 0.5

☆ A Decimal Number contains a Decimal Point. It separates the whole number part from the fractional part of a decimal number.

☆ Let's review decimal place values: Example: **45.3861**

4: tens	5: ones	3: tenths
8: hundredths	6: thousandths	1: tens thousandths

☆ To compare two decimals, compare each digit of two decimals in the same place value. Start from left. Compare hundreds, tens, ones, tenth, hundredth, etc.

☆ To compare numbers, use these symbols:

Equal to =	Less than <	Greater than >
Greater than or equal ≥	Less than or equal ≤	

Examples:

Example 1. Compare 0.07 and 0.70.

Solution: 0.70 is greater than 0.07, because the tenth place of 0.70 is 7, but the tenth place of 0.07 is zero. Then: $0.07 < 0.70$

Example 2. Compare 0.0413 and 0.413.

Solution: 0.413 is greater than 0.0413, because the tenth place of 0.413 is 4, but the tenth place of 0.0413 is zero. Then: $0.0413 < 0.413$

Rounding Decimals

☆ We can round decimals to a certain accuracy or number of decimal places. This is used to make calculations easier to do and results easier to understand when exact values are not too important.

☆ First, you'll need to remember your place values: For example: **12.4869**

    1: tens   2: ones   4: tenths

    8: hundredths   6: thousandths   9: tens thousandths

☆ To round a decimal, first find the place value you'll round to.

☆ Find the digit to the right of the place value you're rounding to. If it is 5 or bigger, add 1 to the place value you're rounding to and remove all digits on its right side. If the digit to the right of the place value is less than 5, keep the place value and remove all digits on the right.

Examples:

Example 1. Round 2.2768 to the thousandth place value.

Solution: First, look at the next place value to the right, (tens thousandths). It's 8 and it is greater than 5. Thus add 1 to the digit in the thousandth place. The thousandth place is 6. → $6 + 1 = 7$, then, the answer is 2.277

Example 2. Round 5.6249 to the nearest hundredth.

Solution: First, look at the digit to the right of hundredth (thousandths place value). It's 4 and it is less than 5, thus remove all the digits to the right of hundredth place. Then, the answer is 5.62

Adding and Subtracting Decimals

☆ Line up the decimal numbers.

☆ Add zeros to have the same number of digits for both numbers if necessary.

☆ Remember your place values: For example: 73.5196

7: tens	3: ones	5: tenths
1: hundredths	9: thousandths	6: tens thousandths

☆ Add or subtract using column addition or subtraction.

Examples:

Example 1. Find the difference. $3.58 - 2.23$

Solution: First, line up the numbers: $\begin{array}{r} 3.58 \\ -2.23 \\ \hline \end{array}$ → Start with the hundredths place:

$8 - 3 = 5$, $\begin{array}{r} 3.58 \\ -2.23 \\ \hline 5 \end{array}$ → Continue with tenths place. $5 - 2 = 3$, $\begin{array}{r} 3.58 \\ -2.23 \\ \hline .35 \end{array}$ → Subtract the

ones place. $3 - 2 = 1$, $\begin{array}{r} 3.58 \\ -2.23 \\ \hline 1.35 \end{array}$

Example 2. Add. $2.8 + 3.12$

Solution: First, line up the numbers: $\begin{array}{r} 2.8 \\ +3.12 \\ \hline \end{array}$ → Add a zero to have the same

number of digits for both numbers. $\begin{array}{r} 2.80 \\ +3.12 \\ \hline \end{array}$ → Start with the hundredths place:

$0 + 2 = 2$, $\begin{array}{r} 2.80 \\ +3.12 \\ \hline 2 \end{array}$ → Continue with tenths place: $8 + 1 = 9$, $\begin{array}{r} 2.80 \\ +3.12 \\ \hline .92 \end{array}$ → Add the ones

place: $3 + 2 = 5$, $\begin{array}{r} 2.80 \\ +3.12 \\ \hline 5.92 \end{array}$ The answer is 5.92.

bit.ly/38uyUdx

Find more at

Multiplying and Dividing Decimals

For multiplying decimals:

☆ Ignore the decimal point and set up and multiply the numbers as you do with whole numbers.

☆ Count the total number of decimal places in both of the factors.

☆ Place the decimal point in the product.

☆ For dividing decimals:

☆ If the divisor is not a whole number, move the decimal point to the right to make it a whole number. Do the same for the dividend.

☆ Divide similar to whole numbers.

$$\begin{array}{r} 45 \\ \times\ 34 \\ \hline 180 \\ 135\ \\ \hline .1530 \end{array}$$

Examples:

Example 1. Find the product. $0.45 \times 0.34 =$

Solution: Set up and multiply the numbers as you do with whole numbers. Line up the numbers: $\begin{array}{r}45\\ \times 34\\ \hline\end{array}$ → Start with the ones place then continue with other digits → $\begin{array}{r}45\\ \times 34\\ \hline 1,530\end{array}$. Count the total number of decimal places in both of the factors. There are four decimals digits. (two for each factor 0.45 and 0.34) Then: $0.45 \times 0.34 = 0.1530 = 0.153$

Example 2. Find the quotient. $1.50 \div 0.5 =$

Solution: The divisor is not a whole number. Multiply it by 10 to get 5:
→ $0.5 \times 10 = 5$ Do the same for the dividend to get 15. →
$1.50 \times 10 = 15$
Now, divide $15 \div 5 = 3$. The answer is 3.

Day 3: Practices

✍ Compare. Use >, =, and <

1) $3.2 \boxed{>} 2.5$

2) $4.8 \boxed{<} 8.4$

3) $0.05 \boxed{<} 0.08$

4) $0.12 \boxed{>} 0.09$

5) $0.005 \boxed{<} 0.05$

6) $2.02 \boxed{<} 20.020$

✍ Round each decimal to the nearest whole number.

7) 6.8

8) 15.9

9) 13.41

10) 16.78

11) 67.58

12) 42.67

✍ Find the sum or difference.

13) $98.8 - 56.6 =$

14) $28.45 + 13.22 =$

15) $16.78 + 45.11 =$

16) $86.16 - 72.12 =$

17) $96.23 - 28.32 =$

18) $57.33 + 67.46 =$

19) $46.26 - 39.49 =$

20) $44.95 + 76.53 =$

✍ Find the product or quotient.

21) $8.6 \div 0.2 = \frac{86}{2} = 43$

22) $9.9 \times 0.8 =$

23) $1.84 \div 0.2 = 16.4 \div 2$

24) $2.1 \times 8.4 =$

25) $1.6 \times 4.5 =$

26) $9.2 \times 3.1 =$

Effortless Math Education

Day 3: Answers

1) >

2) <

3) <

4) >

5) <

6) <

7) 7

8) 16

9) 13

10) 17

11) 68

12) 43

13) 42.2

14) 41.67

15) 61.89

16) 14.04

17) 67.91

18) 124.79

19) 6.77

20) 121.48

21) 43

22) 7.92

23) 9.2

24) 17.64

25) 7.2

26) 28.52

Effortless Math Education

DAY 4 Integers

Math topics that you'll learn in this chapter:

1. Adding and subtracting Integers

2. Multiplying and Dividing Integers

3. Order of Operations

4. Integers and Absolute Value

23

Adding and Subtracting Integers

☆ Integers include zero, counting numbers, and the negative of the counting numbers. $\{\dots, -3, -2, -1, 0, 1, 2, 3, \dots\}$

☆ Add a positive integer by moving to the right on the number line. (you will get a bigger number)

☆ Add a negative integer by moving to the left on the number line. (you will get a smaller number)

☆ Subtract an integer by adding its opposite.

Number line

Examples:

Example 1. Solve. $5 + (-9) =$ 14

Solution: Keep the first number and convert the sign of the second number to its opposite. (change subtraction into addition. Then: $5 + 9 = 14$

Example 2. Solve. $7 + (3 - 8) =$ 2

Solution: First, subtract the numbers in brackets, $3 - 8 = -5$.
Then: $7 + (-5) = \rightarrow$ change addition into subtraction: $7 - 5 = 2$

Example 3. Solve. $(6 - 12) + 11 =$ 5

Solution: First, subtract the numbers in brackets, $6 - 12 = -6$
Then: $-6 + 11 = \rightarrow -6 + 11 = 5$

Example 4. Solve. $15 + (-7 - 8) =$

Solution: First, subtract the numbers in brackets, $-7 - 8 = -15$
Then: $15 + (-15) = \rightarrow$ change addition into subtraction:
$15 - 15 = 0$

bit.ly/3aKx5vl

Find more at

Multiplying and Dividing Integers

Use the following rules for multiplying and dividing integers:

★ (negative) × (negative) = positive

★ (negative) ÷ (negative) = positive

★ (negative) × (positive) = negative

★ (negative) ÷ (positive) = negative

★ (positive) × (positive) = positive

★ (positive) ÷ (negative) = negative

Examples:

Example 1. Solve. $5 \times (-2) =$ -10

Solution: Use this rule: (positive) × (negative) = negative.
Then: $(5) \times (-2) = -10$

Example 2. Solve. $(-4) + (-21 \div 3) =$ $-4 + -7 = -11$

Solution: First, divide -21 by 3, the numbers in brackets, use this rule:
(negative) ÷ (positive) = negative. Then: $-21 \div 3 = -7$
$(-4) + (-21 \div 3) = (-4) + (-7) = -4 - 7 = -11$

Example 3. Solve. $(10 - 18) \times (-3) =$ $-8 \cdot -3 = -24$

Solution: First, subtract the numbers in brackets,
$10 - 18 = -8 \rightarrow (-8) \times (-3) =$
Now use this rule: (negative) × (negative) = positive $\rightarrow (-8) \times (-3) = 24$

Order of Operations

☆ In Mathematics, "operations" are addition, subtraction, multiplication, division, exponentiation (written as b^n), and grouping.

☆ When there is more than one math operation in an expression, use PEMDAS: (to memorize this rule, remember the phrase "Please Excuse My Dear Aunt Sally".)

- ❖ Parentheses

- ❖ Exponents

- ❖ Multiplication and Division (from left to right)

- ❖ Addition and Subtraction (from left to right)

Examples:

Example 1. Solve. $(5 \times 4) - (16 - 5) =$

Solution: First, calculate within parentheses: $(5 \times 4) - (16 - 5) = (20) - (11)$, Then: $(20) - (11) = 9$

Example 2. Solve. $(32 \div 4) + (-17 + 3) =$ $8 + -14 = -6$

Solution: First, calculate within parentheses:
$(32 \div 4) + (-17 + 3) = (8) + (-14)$ Then: $(8) - (14) = -6$

Example 3. Calculate. $(8 + 4) \div (3^2 \div 3) =$

Solution: First, simplify inside parentheses:
$(12) \div (9 \div 3) = (12) \div (3)$, Then: $(12) \div (3) = 4$

Example 4. Calculate. $3[(4 \times 7) \div (7 \times 2)] =$

Solution: First, calculate within parentheses:
$3[(4 \times 7) \div (7 \times 2)] = 3[(28) \div (14)] = 3[2]$
Multiply 3 and 2. Then: $3[2] = 6$

bit.ly/37LBw7X

Find more at

Integers and Absolute Value

☆ The absolute value of a number is its distance from zero, in either direction, on the number line. For example, the distance of 9 and -9 from zero on number line is 9.

☆ The absolute value of an integer is the numerical value without its sign. (negative or positive)

☆ The vertical bar is used for absolute value as in $|x|$.

☆ The absolute value of a number is never negative; because it only shows, "how far the number is from zero".

Examples:

Example 1. Calculate. $|15 - 3| \times 5 =$

Solution: First, solve $|15 - 3|$, $\rightarrow |15 - 3| = |12|$, the absolute value of 12 is 12, $|12| = 12$, Then: $12 \times 5 = 60$

Example 2. Solve. $\frac{|-12|}{3} \times |7 - 9| =$

Solution: First, find $|-12| \rightarrow$ the absolute value of -12 is 12.
Then: $|-12| = 12$, $\frac{12}{3} \times |7 - 9| =$

Now, calculate $|7 - 9|$, $\rightarrow |7 - 9| = |-2|$, the absolute value of -2 is 2. $|-2| = 2$
Then: $\frac{12}{3} \times 2 = 4 \times 2 = 8$

Example 3. Solve. $|10 - 4| \times \frac{|-5 \times 6|}{3} =$

Solution: First, calculate $|10 - 4|$, $\rightarrow |10 - 4| = |6|$, the absolute value of 6 is 6, $|6| = 6$. Then: $6 \times \frac{|-5 \times 6|}{3}$

Now calculate $|-5 \times 6|$, $\rightarrow |-5 \times 6| = |-30|$, the absolute value of -30 is 30, $|-30| = 30$, Then: $6 \times \frac{30}{3} = 6 \times 10 = 60$

Day 4: Practices

✏ Find each sum or difference.

1) $(-13) + (-4) =$

2) $25 + (3 - 10) =$

3) $12 - (-6 + 9) =$

4) $5 - (-2 + 7) =$

5) $(-11) + (-5 + 6) =$

6) $(-3) + (9 - 16) =$

✏ Solve.

7) $(-12 + 3) \times (-5) =$

8) $(-3 + 4) \times (-11) =$

9) $(-9) \times (6 - 5) =$

10) $(-3 - 7) \times (-6) =$

11) $(-7 + 3) \times (-9 + 6) =$

12) $(-15) \div (-17 + 12) =$

✏ Evaluate each expression.

13) $(-9 \times 2) + 6 =$

14) $(7 \times 3) - (-5) =$

15) $(-8) + (2 \times 7) =$

16) $(9 - 6) + (3 \times 4) =$

17) $(-19 + 5) + (6 \times 2) =$

18) $(32 \div 4) + (1 - 13) =$

✏ Find the answers.

19) $|-9| + |1 - 9| =$

20) $|-7| - |8 - 12| =$

21) $|9 - 11| + |8 - 15| =$

22) $|-7 + 10| - |-8 + 3| =$

23) $|-12 + 6| - |3 - 9| =$

24) $5 + |2 - 6| + |3 - 4| =$

Effortless
Math
Education

Day 4: Answers

1)	−17	13)	−12
2)	18	14)	26
3)	9	15)	6
4)	0	16)	15
5)	−10	17)	−2
6)	−10	18)	−4
7)	45	19)	17
8)	−11	20)	3
9)	−9	21)	9
10)	60	22)	−2
11)	12	23)	0
12)	3	24)	10

Effortless
Math
Education

DAY 5 — Ratios and Proportions

Math topics that you'll learn in this chapter:

1. Simplifying Ratios
2. Proportional Ratios
3. Similarity and Ratios

31

Simplifying Ratios

☆ Ratios are used to make comparisons between two numbers.

☆ Ratios can be written as a fraction, using the word "to", or with a colon.
Example: $\frac{3}{4}$ or "3 to 4" or $3:4$

☆ You can calculate equivalent ratios by multiplying or dividing both sides of the ratio by the same number.

Examples:

Example 1. Simplify. $6:3 =$

Solution: Both numbers 6 and 3 are divisible by $3 \Rightarrow 6 \div 3 = 2$,
$3 \div 3 = 1$, Then: $6:3 = 2:1$

Example 2. There are 26 students in a class and 12 are girls. Find the ratio of girls to boys in that class.

Solution: Subtract 12 from 26 to find the number of boys in the class.
$26 - 12 = 14$. There are 14 boys in the class. So, the ratio of girls to boys is $12:14$. Now, simplify this ratio. Both 14 and 12 are divisible by 2.
Then: $14 \div 2 = 7$, and $12 \div 2 = 6$. In the simplest form, this ratio is $6:7$

Example 3. A recipe calls for butter and sugar in the ratio $4:5$. If you're using 16 cups of butter, how many cups of sugar should you use?

Solution: Since you use 16 cups of butter, or 4 times as much, you need to multiply the amount of sugar by 4. Then: $4 \times 5 = 20$. So, you need to use 20 cups of sugar. You can solve this using equivalent fractions: $\frac{4}{5} = \frac{16}{20}$

14:12

7:6

Proportional Ratios

☆ Two ratios are proportional if they represent the same relationship.

☆ A proportion means that two ratios are equal. It can be written in two ways:

$$\frac{a}{b} = \frac{c}{d} \qquad a : b = c : d$$

☆ The proportion $\frac{a}{b} = \frac{c}{d}$ can be written as: $a \times d = c \times b$

Examples:

Example 1. Solve this proportion for x. $\frac{2}{5} = \frac{8}{x}$

Solution: Use cross multiplication: $\frac{2}{5} = \frac{8}{x} \Rightarrow 2 \times x = 8 \times 5 \Rightarrow 2x = 40$

Divide both sides by 2 to find x: $x = \frac{40}{2} \Rightarrow x = 20$

Example 2. If a box contains red and blue balls in ratio of $4 : 5$ red to blue, how many red balls are there if 50 blue balls are in the box?

Solution: Write a proportion and solve. $\frac{4}{5} = \frac{x}{50}$

Use cross multiplication: $4 \times 50 = 5 \times x \Rightarrow 200 = 5x$
Divide to find x: $x = \frac{200}{5} \Rightarrow x = 40$. There are 40 red balls in the box.

Example 3. Solve this proportion for x. $\frac{6}{7} = \frac{18}{x}$

Solution: Use cross multiplication: $\frac{6}{7} = \frac{18}{x} \Rightarrow 6 \times x = 7 \times 18 \Rightarrow 6x = 126$

Divide to find x: $x = \frac{126}{6} \Rightarrow x = 21$

Example 4. Solve this proportion for x. $\frac{5}{8} = \frac{25}{x}$

Solution: Use cross multiplication: $\frac{5}{8} = \frac{25}{x} \Rightarrow 5 \times x = 8 \times 25 \Rightarrow$
$5x = 200$
Divide to find x: $x = \frac{200}{5} \Rightarrow x = 40$

Similarity and Ratios

☆ Two figures are similar if they have the same shape.

☆ Two or more figures are similar if the corresponding angles are equal, and the corresponding sides are in proportion.

Examples:

Example 1. The following triangles are similar. What is the value of the unknown side?

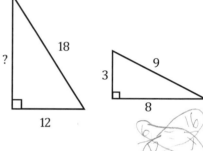

Solution: Find the corresponding sides and write a proportion.
$\frac{9}{18} = \frac{8}{x}$. Now, use the cross product to solve for x:
$\frac{9}{18} = \frac{8}{x} \rightarrow 9 \times x = 18 \times 8 \rightarrow 9x = 144$. Divide both sides by 9. Then: $9x = 144 \rightarrow x = \frac{144}{9} \rightarrow x = 16$

The missing side is 16.

Example 2. Two rectangles are similar. The first is 6 feet wide and 16 feet long. The second is 12 feet wide. What is the length of the second rectangle?

Solution: Let's put x for the length of the second rectangle. Since two rectangles are similar, their corresponding sides are in proportion. Write a proportion and solve for the missing number.
$\frac{6}{12} = \frac{16}{x} \rightarrow 6x = 12 \times 16 \rightarrow 6x = 192 \rightarrow x = \frac{192}{6} = 32$
The length of the second rectangle is 32 feet.

Day 5: Practices

✎ Reduce each ratio.

1) $2:18 = \underline{1}:\underline{9}$

2) $5:35 = \underline{1}:\underline{7}$

3) $8:72 = \underline{1}:\underline{9}$

4) $24:36 = \underline{2}:\underline{3}$

5) $25:40 = \underline{5}:\underline{8}$

6) $40:72 = \underline{5}:\underline{9}$

7) $28:63 = \underline{4}:\underline{9}$

8) $18:81 = \underline{2}:\underline{9}$

✎ Solve each problem.

9) Bob has 16 red cards and 20 green cards. What is the ratio of Bob's red cards to his green cards? $\underline{4:5}$

$16:20$
$4:5$

✎ Solve each proportion.

10) $\frac{7}{2} = \frac{x}{4} \Rightarrow x = \underline{14}$ $\frac{28 = 2x}{2}$

11) $\frac{9}{6} = \frac{x}{2} \Rightarrow x = \underline{3}$ $\frac{18 = 6x}{6}$

12) $\frac{3}{6} = \frac{5}{x} \Rightarrow x = \underline{10}$ $\frac{30 = 3x}{3}$
$x = 10$

13) $\frac{7}{x} = \frac{2}{6} \Rightarrow x = \underline{21}$

14) $\frac{3}{9} = \frac{5}{x} \Rightarrow x = \underline{\hphantom{00}}$

15) $\frac{4}{18} = \frac{2}{x} \Rightarrow x = \underline{\hphantom{00}}$

16) $\frac{6}{16} = \frac{3}{x} \Rightarrow x = \underline{\hphantom{00}}$

17) $\frac{28}{8} = \frac{x}{2} \Rightarrow x = \underline{\hphantom{00}}$

✎ Solve.

$\frac{2x = 42}{2}$
$x = 21$

18) Two rectangles are similar. The first is 8 feet wide and 32 feet long. The second is 12 feet wide.

What is the length of the second rectangle? $\underline{\hphantom{000}48\hphantom{000}}$

Day 5: Answers

1) $1:9$

2) $1:7$

3) $1:9$

4) $2:3$

5) $5:8$

6) $5:9$

7) $4:9$

8) $2:9$

9) $4:5$

10) 14

11) 3

12) 10

13) 21

14) 15

15) 9

16) 8

17) 7

18) 48 meters

Effortless Math Education

DAY 6 Percent

Math topics that you'll learn in this chapter:

1. Percent Problems
2. Percent of increase and Decrease
3. Discount, Tax and Tip
4. Simple Interest

37

Percent Problems

☆ Percent is a ratio of a number and 100. It always has the same denominator, 100. The percent symbol is "%".

☆ Percent means "per 100". So, 20% is $\frac{20}{100}$.

☆ In each percent problem, we are looking for the base, or the part or the percent.

☆ Use these equations to find each missing section in a percent problem:

- ❖ Base = Part ÷ Percent
- ❖ Part = Percent × Base
- ❖ Percent = Part ÷ Base

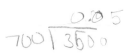

Examples:

Example 1. What is 10% of 35?

Solution: In this problem, we have the percent (10%) and the base (35) and we are looking for the "part". Use this formula: *Part = Percent × Base*.
Then: $Part = 10\% \times 35 = \frac{10}{100} \times 35 = 0.10 \times 35 = 3.5$. The answer: 10% of 35 is 3.5.

Example 2. 35 is what percent of 700?

Solution: In this problem, we are looking for the percent. Use this equation:
Percent = Part ÷ Base → *Percent* = 35 ÷ 700 = 0.05 = 5%.
Then: 35 is 5 percent of 700.

Example 3. 90 is 40 percent of what number?

Solution: In this problem, we are looking for the base. Use this equation:
Base = Part ÷ Percent → *Base* = 90 ÷ 40% = 90 ÷ 0.40 = 225
Then: 90 is 40 percent of 225.

Percent of Increase and Decrease

☆ Percent of change (increase or decrease) is a mathematical concept that represents the degree of change over time.

☆ To find the percentage of increase or decrease:

1. New Number – Original Number

2. (The result ÷ Original Number) × 100

☆ Or use this formula: Percent of change $= \dfrac{new\ number - original\ number}{original\ number} \times 100$

☆ Note: If your answer is a negative number, then this is a percentage decrease. If it is positive, then this is a percentage increase.

$$\frac{25-20}{20} = \frac{5}{20} = \frac{1}{4} \cdot 100 = 25\%$$

Examples:

Example 1. The price of a shirt increases from $20 to $25. What is the percentage increase?

Solution: First, find the difference: $25 - 20 = 5$

Then: $(5 \div 20) \times 100 = \dfrac{5}{20} \times 100 = 25$. The percentage increase is 25%. It means that the price of the shirt increased by 25%.

Example 2. The price of a table decreased from $40 to $35. What is the percent of decrease?

$$\frac{35-40}{40} = \frac{-5}{40} = \frac{-1}{8} \cdot 100$$

Solution: Use this formula:

$$Percent\ of\ change = \frac{new\ number - original\ number}{original\ number} \times 100 =$$

$\dfrac{35-40}{40} \times 100 = \dfrac{-5}{40} \times 100 = -12.5$. The percentage decrease is 12.5. (the negative sign means percentage decrease) Therefore, the price of the table decreased by 12.5%.

Discount, Tax and Tip

☆ To find the discount: Multiply the regular price by the rate of discount

☆ To find the selling price: Original price − discount

☆ To find tax: Multiply the tax rate to the taxable amount (income, property value, etc.)

☆ To find the tip, multiply the rate to the selling price.

$$.30 \bullet X = \frac{60}{.30}$$

Examples:

Example 1. With an 30% discount, Ella saved $60 on a dress. What was the original price of the dress?

Solution: let x be the original price of the dress. Then: 30% *of* $x = 60$. Write an equation and solve for x: $0.30 \times x = 60 \rightarrow x = \frac{60}{0.30} = 200$. The original price of the dress was $200.

Example 2. Sophia purchased a new computer for a price of $630 at the Apple Store. What is the total amount her credit card is charged if the sales tax is 5%?

Solution: The taxable amount is $630, and the tax rate is 5%. Then:
$$Tax = 0.05 \times 630 = 31.5$$
Final price = Selling price + Tax → final price = $630 + $31.5 = $661.5

Example 3. Nicole and her friends went out to eat at a restaurant. If their bill was $80.00 and they gave their server a 12% tip, how much did they pay altogether?

Solution: First, find the tip. To find the tip, multiply the rate to the bill amount. $Tip = 80 \times 0.12 = 9.6$. The final price is: $80 + $9.6 = $89.6

bit.ly/2Je5lo0

Find more at

Simple Interest

☆ Simple Interest: The charge for borrowing money or the return for lending it.

☆ Simple interest is calculated on the initial amount (principal).

☆ To solve a simple interest problem, use this formula:

$$Interest = principal \times rate \times time \quad (I = p \times r \times t = prt)$$

Examples:

Example 1. Find simple interest for $300 investment at 5% for 4 years.

Solution: Use Interest formula:
$I = prt$ ($P = \$300$, $r = 5\% = \frac{5}{100} = 0.05$ and $t = 4$) Then: $I = 300 \times 0.05 \times 4 = \$60$

Example 2. Find simple interest for $1,500 at 6% for 5 years.

Solution: Use Interest formula:
$I = prt$ ($P = \$1,500$, $r = 6\% = \frac{6}{100} = 0.06$ and $t = 5$)
Then: $I = 1,500 \times 0.06 \times 5 = \$450$

Example 3. Andy received a student loan to pay for his educational expenses this year. What is the interest on the loan if he borrowed $3,600 at 8% for 5 years?

Solution: Use Interest formula: $I = prt$. $P = \$3,600$, $r = 8\% = 0.08$ and $t = 5$
Then: $I = 3,600 \times 0.08 \times 5 = \$1,440$

Example 4. Bob is starting his own small business. He borrowed $10,000 from the bank at an 6% rate for 6 months. Find the interest Bob will pay on this loan.

Solution: Use Interest formula: $I = prt$. $P = \$10,000$, $r = 6\% = 0.06$ and $t = 0.5$ (6 months is half year). Then:
$$I = 10,000 \times 0.06 \times 0.5 = \$300$$

Day 6: Practices

✍ Solve each problem.

1) What is 18% of 40? ____

2) 90 is what percent of 200? ____%

3) 60 is what percent of 300? ____%

4) 22 is 20% of what number? ____

✍ Solve each problem.

5) At a Coffee Shop, the price of a cup of coffee increased from $1.35 to $1.62. What is the percent increase in the cost of the coffee? ____ %

6) A $45 shirt now selling for $36 is discounted by what percent? ____ %

✍ Find the selling price of each item.

7) Original price of a laptop: $450

   Tax: 10%, Selling price: $_____

8) Mason has lunch at a restaurant and the cost of his meal is $40. Mason wants to leave a 20% tip. What is Mason's total bill, including tip? $_____

✍ Determine the simple interest for the following loans.

9) $1,000 at 5% for 4 years. $__

10) $400 at 3% for 5 years. $__

11) $240 at 4% for 3 years. $__

12) $500 at 4.5% for 6 years. $__

Effortless Math Education

Day 6: Answers

1) 7.2

2) 45%

3) 20%

4) 110

5) 20%

6) 20%

7) $495.00

8) $48.00

9) $200.00

10) $60.00

11) $28.80

12) $135.00

Effortless Math Education

DAY 7 Exponents and Variables

Math topics that you'll learn in this chapter:

1. Multiplication Property of Exponents

2. Division Property of Exponents

3. Powers of Products and Quotients

4. Zero and Negative Exponents

45

Multiplication Property of Exponents

☆ Exponents are shorthand for repeated multiplication of the same number by itself. For example, instead of 2×2, we can write 2^2. For $3 \times 3 \times 3 \times 3$, we can write 3^4

☆ In algebra, a variable is a letter used to stand for a number. The most common letters are: x, y, z, a, b, c, m, and n.

☆ Exponent's rules: $x^a \times x^b = x^{a+b}$, $\dfrac{x^a}{x^b} = x^{a-b}$

$$(x^a)^b = x^{a \times b} \qquad\qquad (xy)^a = x^a \times y^a \qquad\qquad \left(\dfrac{a}{b}\right)^c = \dfrac{a^c}{b^c}$$

Examples:

Example 1. Multiply. $4x^3 \times 2x^5$

Solution: Use Exponent's rules: $x^a \times x^b = x^{a+b} \rightarrow x^3 \times x^5 = x^{3+5} = x^8$
Then: $4x^3 \times 2x^5 = 8x^8$

Example 2. Simplify. $\left(x^5 y^3\right)^2$

Solution: Use Exponent's rules: $(x^a)^b = x^{a \times b}$.
Then: $\left(x^5 y^3\right)^2 = x^{5 \times 2} y^{3 \times 2} = x^{10} y^6$

Example 3. Multiply. $3x^6 \times 9x^8$

Solution: Use Exponent's rules: $x^a \times x^b = x^{a+b} \rightarrow x^6 \times x^8 = x^{6+8} = x^{14}$
Then: $3x^6 \times 9x^8 = 27x^{14}$

Example 4. Simplify. $\left(2x^3 y^5\right)^3$

Solution: Use Exponent's rules: $(x^a)^b = x^{a \times b}$.
Then: $\left(2x^3 y^5\right)^3 = 2^3 x^{3 \times 3} y^{5 \times 3} = 8x^9 y^{15}$

Division Property of Exponents

For division of exponents use following formulas:

☆ $\frac{x^a}{x^b} = x^{a-b}$ $(x \neq 0)$

☆ $\frac{x^a}{x^b} = \frac{1}{x^{b-a}}$, $(x \neq 0)$

☆ $\frac{1}{x^b} = x^{-b}$

Examples:

Example 1. Simplify. $\frac{18x^2y^2}{2xy^3} =$

Solution: First, cancel the common factor: $2 \rightarrow \frac{18x^2y^2}{2xy^3} = \frac{9x^2y^2}{xy^3}$

Use Exponent's rules: $\frac{x^a}{x^b} = x^{a-b} \rightarrow \frac{x^2}{x} = x^{2-1} = x$ and $\frac{x^a}{x^b} = \frac{1}{x^{b-a}} \rightarrow \frac{y^2}{y^3} = \frac{1}{y^{3-2}} = \frac{1}{y}$

Then: $\frac{18x^2y^2}{2y^3} = \frac{9x}{y}$

$$\frac{18x^2y^2}{2xy^3} = \frac{9x^2y^2}{xy^3} = \frac{9x}{y}$$

Example 2. Simplify. $\frac{32x^7}{4x^5} =$

Solution: Use Exponent's rules: $\frac{x^a}{x^b} = x^{a-b} \rightarrow \frac{x^7}{x^5} = x^{7-5} = x^2$

Then: $\frac{32x^7}{4x^5} = 8x^2$

$$\frac{32x^7}{4x^5} = 8x^2$$

Example 3. Simplify. $\frac{6x^4y^2}{54x^3y} =$

Solution: First, cancel the common factor 6: $\rightarrow \frac{x^4y^2}{9x^3y}$

Use Exponent's rules: $\frac{x^a}{x^b} = x^{a-b} \rightarrow \frac{x^4}{x^3} = x^{4-3} = x$ and $\frac{y^2}{y} = y$

Then: $\frac{6x^4y^2}{54x^3y} = \frac{xy}{9}$

$$\frac{6x^4y^2}{54x^3y} = \frac{x^4y^2}{9x^3y} = \frac{xy^2}{9y} = \frac{xy}{9y}$$

Powers of Products and Quotients

☆ For any nonzero numbers a and b and any integer x, $(ab)^x = a^x \times b^x$

and $\left(\frac{a}{b}\right)^c = \frac{a^c}{b^c}$

Examples:

Example 1. Simplify. $(5x^4y^2)^2$

Solution: Use Exponent's rules: $(x^a)^b = x^{a \times b}$

$(5x^4y^2)^2 = (5)^2(x^4)^2(y^2)^2 = 25x^{4\times2}y^{2\times2} = 25x^8y^4$

Example 2. Simplify. $\left(\frac{3x^3}{4x^2}\right)^2$

Solution: First, cancel the common factor: $x \rightarrow \left(\frac{3x^3}{4x^2}\right)^2 = \left(\frac{3x}{4}\right)^2$

Use Exponent's rules: $\left(\frac{a}{b}\right)^c = \frac{a^c}{b^c}$, Then: $\left(\frac{3x}{4}\right)^2 = \frac{(3x)^2}{(4)^2} = \frac{9x^2}{16}$

Example 3. Simplify. $(-3x^4y^6)^2$

Solution: Use Exponent's rules: $(x^a)^b = x^{a \times b}$

$(-3x^4y^6)^2 = (-3)^2(x^4)^2(y^6)^2 = 9x^{4\times2}y^{6\times2} = 9x^8y^{12}$

Example 4. Simplify. $\left(\frac{3x}{7x^2}\right)^2$

Solution: First, cancel the common factor: $x \rightarrow \left(\frac{3x}{7x^2}\right)^2 = \left(\frac{3}{7x}\right)^2$

Use Exponent's rules: $\left(\frac{a}{b}\right)^c = \frac{a^c}{b^c}$, Then: $\left(\frac{3}{7x}\right)^2 = \frac{3^2}{(7x)^2} = \frac{9}{49x^2}$

bit.ly/34CgPJm

Zero and Negative Exponents

☆ Zero-Exponent Rule: $a^0 = 1$, this means that anything raised to the zero power is 1. For example: $(5xy)^0 = 1$ (number zero is an exception: $\mathbf{0^0 = 0}$)

☆ A negative exponent simply means that the base is on the wrong side of the fraction line, so you need to flip the base to the other side. For instance, "x^{-2}" (pronounced as "ecks to the minus two") just means "x^2" but underneath, as in $\frac{1}{x^2}$.

Examples:

Example 1. Evaluate. $\left(\frac{2}{3}\right)^{-2} =$

Solution: Use negative exponent's rule: $\left(\frac{x^a}{x^b}\right)^{-2} = \left(\frac{x^b}{x^a}\right)^2 \rightarrow \left(\frac{2}{3}\right)^{-2} = \left(\frac{3}{2}\right)^2$

Then: $\left(\frac{3}{2}\right)^2 = \frac{3^2}{2^2} = \frac{9}{4}$

Example 2. Evaluate. $\left(\frac{3}{4}\right)^{-3} =$

Solution: Use negative exponent's rule: $\left(\frac{x^a}{x^b}\right)^{-3} = \left(\frac{x^b}{x^a}\right)^3 \rightarrow \left(\frac{3}{4}\right)^{-3} = \left(\frac{4}{3}\right)^3 =$

Then: $\left(\frac{4}{3}\right)^3 = \frac{4^3}{3^3} = \frac{64}{27}$

Example 3. Evaluate. $\left(\frac{x}{y}\right)^0 =$

Solution: Use zero-exponent Rule: $a^0 = 1$
Then: $\left(\frac{x}{y}\right)^0 = 1$

Example 4. Evaluate. $\left(\frac{12}{19}\right)^{-1} =$

Solution: Use negative exponent's rule: $\left(\frac{x^a}{x^b}\right)^{-1} = \left(\frac{x^b}{x^a}\right)^1 \rightarrow \left(\frac{12}{19}\right)^{-1} =$
$\left(\frac{19}{12}\right)^1 = \frac{19}{12}$

Day 7: Practices

✍ Find the products.

1) $7xy^3 \times 2x^2y =$

2) $-5x^5y^5 \times x^3y^2 =$

3) $-6x^2y^6 \times 5x^4y^2 =$

4) $-3x^3y^3 \times 2x^3y^2 =$

5) $-6x^5y^3 \times 4x^4y^3 =$

6) $-2x^4y^3 \times 5x^6y^2 =$

7) $-7y^6 \times 3x^6y^3 =$

8) $-9x^4 \times 2x^4y^2 =$

✍ Simplify.

9) $\dfrac{15x^5}{5x^3} =$

10) $\dfrac{16x^3}{4x^5} =$

11) $\dfrac{72y^2}{8x^3y^6} =$

12) $\dfrac{10x^3y^4}{50x^2y^3} =$

13) $\dfrac{13y^2}{52x^4y^4} =$

14) $\dfrac{81y^6x}{54x^4y^3} =$

✍ Solve.

15) $(3x^3y^4)^3 =$

16) $(4x \times 6xy^3)^2 =$

17) $\left(\dfrac{9x}{x^3}\right)^2 =$

18) $(\dfrac{3y}{18y^2})^2 =$

19) $\left(\dfrac{3x^2y^3}{24x^4y^2}\right)^3 =$

20) $\left(\dfrac{18x^7y^4}{72x^5y^2}\right)^2 =$

21) $\left(\dfrac{12x^6y^4}{48x^5y^3}\right)^2 =$

✍ Evaluate each expression. (Zero and Negative Exponents)

22) $\left(\dfrac{1}{4}\right)^{-2} =$

23) $\left(\dfrac{1}{3}\right)^{-2} =$

24) $\left(\dfrac{1}{7}\right)^{-3} =$

25) $\left(\dfrac{2}{5}\right)^{-3} =$

26) $\left(\dfrac{2}{3}\right)^{-3} =$

27) $\left(\dfrac{3}{5}\right)^{-4} =$

**Effortless
Math
Education**

Day 7: Answers

1) $14x^3y^4$

2) $-5x^8y^7$

3) $-30x^6y^8$

4) $-6x^6y^5$

5) $-24x^9y^6$

6) $-10x^{10}y^5$

7) $-21x^6y^9$

8) $-18x^8y^2$

9) $3x^2$

10) $\frac{4}{x^2}$

11) $\frac{9}{x^3y^4}$

12) $\frac{xy}{5}$

13) $\frac{1}{4x^4y^2}$

14) $\frac{3y^3}{2x^3}$

15) $27x^9y^{12}$

16) $576x^4y^6$

17) $\frac{81}{x^4}$

18) $\frac{1}{36y^2}$

19) $\frac{y^3}{512x^6}$

20) $\frac{x^4y^4}{16}$

21) $\frac{x^2y^2}{16}$

22) 16

23) 9

24) 343

25) $\frac{125}{8}$

26) $\frac{27}{8}$

27) $\frac{625}{81}$

Effortless Math Education

DAY 8 — Scientific Notation

Math topics that you'll learn in this chapter:

1. Negative Exponents and Negative Bases

2. Scientific Notation

3. Radicals

53

Negative Exponents and Negative Bases

☆ A negative exponent is the reciprocal of that number with a positive exponent.
$(3)^{-2} = \frac{1}{3^2}$

☆ To simplify a negative exponent, make the power positive!

☆ The parenthesis is important! -5^{-2} is not the same as $(-5)^{-2}$

$$-5^{-2} = -\frac{1}{5^2} \text{ and } (-5)^{-2} = +\frac{1}{5^2}$$

Examples:

Example 1. Simplify. $\left(\frac{a}{2c}\right)^{-2} =$

Solution: Use negative exponent's rule: $\left(\frac{x^a}{x^b}\right)^{-2} = \left(\frac{x^b}{x^a}\right)^2 \rightarrow \left(\frac{a}{2c}\right)^{-2} = \left(\frac{2c}{a}\right)^2$

Now use exponent's rule: $\left(\frac{a}{b}\right)^c = \frac{a^c}{b^c} \rightarrow \left(\frac{2c}{a}\right)^2 = \frac{2^2 c^2}{a^2}$

Then: $\frac{2^2 c^2}{a^2} = \frac{4c^2}{a^2}$

Example 2. Simplify. $\left(\frac{2x}{3y}\right)^{-3} =$

Solution: Use negative exponent's rule: $\left(\frac{x^a}{x^b}\right)^{-3} = \left(\frac{x^b}{x^a}\right)^3 \rightarrow \left(\frac{2x}{3y}\right)^{-3} = \left(\frac{3y}{2x}\right)^3$

Now use exponent's rule: $\left(\frac{a}{b}\right)^c = \frac{a^c}{b^c} \rightarrow \left(\frac{3y}{2x}\right)^3 = \frac{3^3 y^3}{2^3 x^3} = \frac{27y^3}{8x^3}$

Example 3. Simplify. $\left(\frac{4a}{2c}\right)^{-2} =$

Solution: Use negative exponent's rule: $\left(\frac{x^a}{x^b}\right)^{-2} = \left(\frac{x^b}{x^a}\right)^2 \rightarrow \left(\frac{4a}{2c}\right)^{-2} = \left(\frac{2c}{4a}\right)^2$

Now use exponent's rule: $\left(\frac{a}{b}\right)^c = \frac{a^c}{b^c} \rightarrow \left(\frac{2c}{4a}\right)^2 = \frac{2^2 c^2}{4^2 a^2}$

Then: $\frac{2^2 c^2}{4^2 a^2} = \frac{4c^2}{16a^2} = \frac{c^2}{4a^2}$

bit.ly/3nPROSM

Find more at

Scientific Notation

☆ Scientific notation is used to write very big or very small numbers in decimal form.

☆ In scientific notation, all numbers are written in the form of: $m \times 10^n$, where m is greater than 1 and less than 10.

☆ To convert a number from scientific notation to standard form, move the decimal point to the left (if the exponent of ten is a negative number), or to the right (if the exponent is positive).

Examples:

Example 1. Write 2.5×10^{-5} in standard notation.

Solution: The exponent is negative 5. Then, move the decimal point to the left five digits. (remember $2.5 = 00000025$) When the decimal moved to the right, the exponent is negative. Then: $2.5 \times 10^{-5} = 0.000025$

Example 2. Write 0.00013 in scientific notation.

Solution: First, move the decimal point to the right so you have a number between 1 and 10. That number is 1.3. Now, determine how many places the decimal moved in step 1 by the power of 10. We moved the decimal point 4 digits to the right. Then: $10^{-4} \rightarrow$ When the decimal moved to the right, the exponent is negative. Then: $0.00013 = 1.3 \times 10^{-4}$

Example 3. Write 0.00046 in scientific notation.

Solution: First, move the decimal point to the right so you have a number between 1 and 10. Then: $m = 4.6$, Now, determine how many places the decimal moved in step 1 by the power of 10. $10^{-4} \rightarrow$ Then: $0.00046 = 4.6 \times 10^{-4}$

Radicals

★ If n is a positive integer and x is a real number, then: $\sqrt[n]{x} = x^{\frac{1}{n}}$,

$$\sqrt[n]{xy} = x^{\frac{1}{n}} \times y^{\frac{1}{n}}, \ \sqrt[n]{\frac{x}{y}} = \frac{x^{\frac{1}{n}}}{y^{\frac{1}{n}}}, \text{ and } \sqrt[n]{x} \times \sqrt[n]{y} = \sqrt[n]{xy}$$

★ A square root of x is a number r whose square is: $r^2 = x$ (r is a square root of x)

★ To add and subtract radicals, we need to have the same values under the radical. For example: $\sqrt{3} + \sqrt{3} = 2\sqrt{3}$, $3\sqrt{5} - \sqrt{5} = 2\sqrt{5}$

Examples:

Example 1. Find the square root of $\sqrt{169}$.

Solution: First, factor the number: $169 = 13^2$, Then: $\sqrt{169} = \sqrt{13^2}$,
Now use radical rule: $\sqrt[n]{a^n} = a$. Then: $\sqrt{169} = \sqrt{13^2} = 13$

Example 2. Evaluate. $\sqrt{9} \times \sqrt{25} =$

Solution: Find the values of $\sqrt{9}$ and $\sqrt{25}$. Then: $\sqrt{9} \times \sqrt{25} = 3 \times 5 = 15$

Example 3. Solve. $7\sqrt{2} + 5\sqrt{2}$.

Solution: Since we have the same values under the radical, we can add these two radicals: $7\sqrt{2} + 5\sqrt{2} = 12\sqrt{2}$

Example 4. Evaluate. $\sqrt{2} \times \sqrt{200} =$

Solution: Use this radical rule: $\sqrt[n]{x} \times \sqrt[n]{y} = \sqrt[n]{xy} \rightarrow \sqrt{2} \times \sqrt{200} = \sqrt{400}$
The square root of 400 is 40. Then: $\sqrt{2} \times \sqrt{200} = \sqrt{400} = 20$

Day 8: Practices

✍ **Write each expression with positive exponents.**

1) $x^{-7} =$

2) $3y^{-5} =$

3) $15y^{-3} =$

4) $-20x^{-4} =$

5) $12a^{-3}b^5 =$

6) $25a^3b^{-4}c^{-3} =$

7) $-4x^5y^{-3}z^{-6} =$

8) $\frac{18y}{x^3y^{-2}} =$

9) $\frac{20a^{-2}b}{-12c^{-4}} =$

✍ **Write each number in scientific notation.**

10) $0.00412 =$

11) $0.0311 =$

12) $0.000053 =$

13) $0.00025 =$

14) $66,000 =$

15) $1,500 =$

16) $72,000,000 =$

17) $1,900,000 =$

✍ **Evaluate.**

18) $\sqrt{8} \times \sqrt{8} =$

19) $\sqrt{5} \times \sqrt{5} =$

20) $\sqrt{9} + \sqrt{16} =$

21) $\sqrt{36} - \sqrt{9} =$

22) $\sqrt{81} + \sqrt{16} =$

23) $\sqrt{4} \times \sqrt{25} =$

24) $\sqrt{2} \times \sqrt{32} =$

25) $4\sqrt{3} + 5\sqrt{3} =$

Day 8: Answers

1) $\dfrac{1}{x^7}$

2) $\dfrac{3}{y^5}$

3) $\dfrac{15}{y^3}$

4) $-\dfrac{20}{x^4}$

5) $\dfrac{12b^5}{a^3}$

6) $\dfrac{25a^3}{b^4c^3}$

7) $-\dfrac{4x^5}{y^3z^6}$

8) $\dfrac{18y^3}{x^3}$

9) $-\dfrac{5bc^4}{3a^2}$

10) 4.12×10^{-3}

11) 3.11×10^{-2}

12) 5.3×10^{-5}

13) 2.5×10^{-4}

14) 6.6×10^4

15) 1.5×10^3

16) 7.2×10^7

17) 1.9×10^6

18) 8

19) 5

20) 7

21) 3

22) 13

23) 10

24) 8

25) $9\sqrt{3}$

**Effortless
Math
Education**

DAY 9 Expressions and Variables

Math topics that you'll learn in this chapter:

1. Simplifying Variable Expressions
2. Simplifying Polynomial Expressions
3. The Distributive Property
4. Evaluating One Variable
5. Evaluating Two Variables

59

Simplifying Variable Expressions

☆ In algebra, a variable is a letter used to stand for a number. The most common letters are x, y, z, a, b, c, m, and n.

☆ An algebraic expression is an expression that contains integers, variables, and math operations such as addition, subtraction, multiplication, division, etc.

☆ In an expression, we can combine "like" terms. (values with same variable and same power)

Examples:

Example 1. Simplify. $(2x + 3x + 5) =$

Solution: In this expression, there are three terms: $2x, \ 3x$, and 5. Two terms are "like terms": $2x$ and $3x$. Combine like terms. $2x + 3x = 5x$. Then: $(2x + 3x + 5) = 5x + 5$ (***remember you cannot combine variables and numbers.***)

Example 2. Simplify. $-4x^2 - 3x + 7x^2 - 6 =$

Solution: Combine "like" terms: $-4x^2 + 7x^2 = 3x^2$.
Then: $-4x^2 - 3x + 7x^2 - 6 = 3x^2 - 3x - 6$.

Example 3. Simplify. $(-5 + 8x^2 + 3x^2 + 4x) =$

Solution: Combine like terms. Then: $(-5 + 8x^2 + 3x^2 + 4x) = 11x^2 + 4x - 5$

Example 4. Simplify. $12x + 7x^2 - 14x + 9x^2 =$

Solution: Combine "like" terms: $12x - 14x = -2x$, and $7x^2 + 9x^2 = 16x^2$
Then: $12x + 7x^2 - 14x + 9x^2 = -2x + 16x^2$.
Write in standard form (biggest powers first):
$-2x + 16x^2 = 16x^2 - 2x$

bit.ly/2WFVudQ
Find more at

Simplifying Polynomial Expressions

✭ In mathematics, a polynomial is an expression consisting of variables and coefficients that involves only the operations of addition, subtraction, multiplication, and non–negative integer exponents of variables.

$$P(x) = a_n x^n + a_{n-1} x^{n-1} + \ldots + a_2 x^2 + a_1 x + a_0$$

✭ Polynomials must always be simplified as much as possible. It means you must add together any like terms. (values with same variable and same power)

Examples:

Example 1. Simplify this Polynomial Expressions. $6x^2 - 5x^3 - 2x^3 + 4x^4$

Solution: Combine "like" terms: $-5x^3 - 2x^3 = -7x^3$
Then: $6x^2 - 5x^3 - 2x^3 + 4x^4 = 6x^2 - 7x^3 + 4x^4$
Now, write the expression in standard form: $6x^2 - 7x^3 + 4x^4 = 4x^4 - 7x^3 + 6x^2$

Example 2. Simplify this expression. $(4x^2 + 2x^3) - (5x^3 - 6x^2) =$

Solution: First, multiply $(-)$ into $(5x^3 - 6x^2)$:
$(4x^2 + 2x^3) - (5x^3 - 6x^2) = 4x^2 + 2x^3 - 5x^3 + 6x^2$
Then combine "like" terms: $4x^2 + 2x^3 - 5x^3 + 6x^2 = 10x^2 - 3x^3$
And write in standard form: $10x^2 - 3x^3 = -3x^3 + 10x^2$

Example 3. Simplify. $2x^3 - 7x^4 - 8x^2 + 12x^4 =$

Solution: Combine "like" terms: $-7x^4 + 12x^4 = 5x^4$
Then: $2x^3 - 7x^4 - 8x^2 + 12x^4 = 2x^3 + 5x^4 - 8x^2$
And write in standard form: $2x^3 + 5x^4 - 8x^2 = 5x^4 + 2x^3 - 8x^2$

bit.ly/2WT5gtn
Find more at

www.EffortlessMath.com   61

The Distributive Property

☆ The distributive property (or the distributive property of multiplication over addition and subtraction) simplifies and solves expressions in the form of: $a(b + c)$ or $a(b - c)$

☆ The distributive property is multiplying a term outside the parentheses by the terms inside.

☆ Distributive Property rule: $a(b + c) = ab + ac$

Examples:

Example 1. Simply using the distributive property. $(9)(x + 5)$

Solution: Use Distributive Property rule: $a(b + c) = ab + ac$

$(9)(x + 5) = (9 \times x) + (9) \times (5) = 9x + 45$

Example 2. Simply. $(-6)(8x - 4)$

Solution: Use Distributive Property rule: $a(b + c) = ab + ac$

$(-6)(8x - 4) = (-6 \times 8x) + (-6) \times (-4) = -48x + 24$

Example 3. Simply. $(8)(2x - 8) - 14x$

Solution: First, simplify $(8)(2x - 8)$ using the distributive property.

Then: $(8)(2x - 8) = 16x - 64$

Now combine like terms: $(8)(2x - 8) - 14x = 16x - 64 - 14x$

In this expression, $16x$ and $-14x$ are "like terms" and we can combine them.

$16x - 14x = 2x$. Then: $16x - 64 - 14x = 2x - 64$

Evaluating One Variable

☆ To evaluate one variable expressions, find the variable and substitute a number for that variable.

☆ Perform the arithmetic operations.

Examples:

Example 1. Calculate this expression for $x = 3$. $6 + 2x$

Solution: First, substitute 3 for x.

Then: $6 + 2x = 6 + 2(3)$

Now, use order of operation to find the answer: $6 + 2(3) = 6 + 6 = 12$

Example 2. Evaluate this expression for $x = -2$. $6x - 7$

Solution: First, substitute -2 for x.

Then: $6x - 7 = 6(-2) - 7$

Now, use order of operation to find the answer: $6(-2) - 7 = -12 - 7 = -19$

Example 3. Find the value of this expression when $x = 5$. $(9 - 4x)$

Solution: First, substitute 5 for x,

Then: $9 - 4x = 9 - 4(5) = 9 - 20 = -11$

Example 4. Solve this expression for $x = -4$. $12 + 9x$

Solution: Substitute -4 for x.

Then: $12 + 9x = 12 + 9(-4) = 12 - 36 = -24$

Evaluating Two Variables

☆ To evaluate an algebraic expression, substitute a number for each variable.

☆ Perform the arithmetic operations to find the value of the expression.

Examples:

Example 1. Evaluate this expression for $x = -1$ and $y = 2$. $(2x + 6y)$

Solution: Substitute -1 for x, and 2 for y.
Then: $2x + 6y = 2(-1) + 6(2) = -2 + 12 = 10$

Example 2. Calculate this expression for $a = 3$ and $b = -1$. $(5a - 3b)$

Solution: First, substitute 3 for a, and -1 for b.
Then: $5a - 3b = 5(3) - 3(-1)$
Now, use order of operation to find the answer: $5(3) - 3(-1) = 15 + 3 = 18$

Example 3. Evaluate this expression. $-8x - 2y$, $x = 5$, $y = -3$

Solution: Substitute 5 for x, and -3 for y and simplify.
Then: $-8x - 2y = -8(5) - 2(-3) = -40 + 6 = -34$

Example 4. Find the value of this expression $3(4a - 5b)$, when $a = -2$ and $b = 4$.

Solution: Substitute -2 for a, and 4 for b.
Then: $3(4a - 5b), = 3\big(4(-2) - 5(4)\big) = 3(-8 - 20) = 3(-28) = -84$

Day 9: Practices

✍ Simplify each expression.

1) $(12x - 5x - 4) =$

2) $(-16x + 24x - 9) =$

3) $-6 + 9x^2 - 3 + x =$

4) $5x^2 + 3x - 10x - 3 =$

✍ Simplify each polynomial.

5) $15x^3 + 11x - 5x^2 - 9x^3 =$

6) $(7x^3 - 3x^2) + (5x^2 - 13x) =$

7) $(12x^4 + 6x^3) + (x^3 - 5x^4) =$

8) $(15x^5 - 8x^3) - (4x^3 + x^2) =$

✍ Use the distributive property to simply each expression.

9) $6(2 - 3x) =$

10) $(-1)(-9 + x) =$

11) $(-6)(3x - 2) =$

12) $(-x + 12)(-4) =$

✍ Evaluate each expression using the value given.

13) $x = 2 \rightarrow 10 - 4x =$

14) $x = 7 \rightarrow 8x - 3 =$

15) $x = 9 \rightarrow 20 - 2x =$

16) $x = -7 \rightarrow 10 - 9x =$

✍ Evaluate each expression using the values given.

17) $a = 3, b = 5 \rightarrow 3a - 5b =$

18) $x = 6, y = 2 \rightarrow 3x - 2y + 8 =$

Effortless
Math
Education

www.EffortlessMath.com ----------------------------------- 65

Day 9: Answers

1) $7x - 4$

2) $8x - 9$

3) $9x^2 + x - 9$

4) $5x^2 - 7x - 3$

5) $6x^3 - 5x^2 + 11x$

6) $7x^3 + 2x^2 - 13x$

7) $7x^4 + 7x^3$

8) $15x^5 - 12x^3 - x^2$

9) $-18x + 12$

10) $-x + 9$

11) $-18x + 12$

12) $4x - 48$

13) 2

14) 53

15) 2

16) 73

17) -16

18) 22

Effortless Math Education

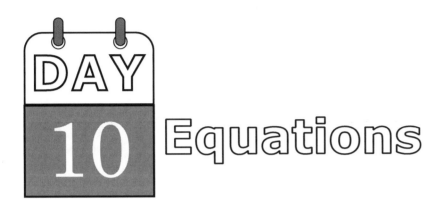

Equations

Math topics that you'll learn in this chapter:

1. One-Step Equations

2. Multi-Step Equations

3. System of Equations

67

One–Step Equations

☆ The values of two expressions on both sides of an equation are equal. Example: $ax = b$. In this equation, ax is equal to b.

☆ Solving an equation means finding the value of the variable.

☆ You only need to perform one Math operation to solve the one-step equations.

☆ To solve a one-step equation, find the inverse (opposite) operation is being performed.

☆ The inverse operations are:

  ❖ Addition and subtraction

  ❖ Multiplication and division

Examples:

Example 1. Solve this equation for x. $3x = 18 \rightarrow x = ?$

Solution: Here, the operation is multiplication (variable x is multiplied by 3) and its inverse operation is division. To solve this equation, divide both sides of equation by 3: $3x = 18 \rightarrow \frac{3x}{3} = \frac{18}{3} \rightarrow x = 6$

Example 2. Solve this equation. $x + 9 = 0 \rightarrow x = ?$

Solution: In this equation, 9 is added to the variable x. The inverse operation of addition is subtraction. To solve this equation, subtract 9 from both sides of the equation: $x + 9 - 9 = 0 - 9$. Then: $x + 9 - 9 = 0 - 9 \rightarrow x = -9$

Example 3. Solve this equation for x. $x - 14 = 0$

Solution: Here, the operation is subtraction and its inverse operation is addition. To solve this equation, add 14 to both sides of the equation: $x - 14 + 14 = 0 + 14 \rightarrow x = 14$

bit.ly/37Jq0tK

Find more at

Multi–Step Equations

☆ To solve a multi-step equation, combine "like" terms on one side.

☆ Bring variables to one side by adding or subtracting.

☆ Simplify using the inverse of addition or subtraction.

☆ Simplify further by using the inverse of multiplication or division.

☆ Check your solution by plugging the value of the variable into the original equation.

Examples:

Example 1. Solve this equation for x. $-5x + 4 = 24$

Solution: Subtract 4 from both sides of the equation.
$-5x + 4 = 24 \rightarrow -5x + 4 - 4 = 24 - 4 \rightarrow -5x = 20$
Divide both sides by -5, then: $-5x = 20 \rightarrow \frac{-5x}{-5} = \frac{20}{-5} \rightarrow x = -4$
Now, check the solution:
$x = -4 \rightarrow -5x + 4 = 24 \rightarrow -5(-4) + 4 = 24 \rightarrow 24 = 24$
The answer $x = -4$ is correct.

Example 2. Solve this equation for x. $2x + 8 = 20 - 2x$

Solution: First, bring variables to one side by adding $2x$ to both sides. Then:
$2x + 8 + 2x = 20 - 2x + 2x \rightarrow 4x + 8 = 20$.
Simplify: $4x + 8 = 20$. Now, subtract 8 from both sides of the equation:
$4x + 8 - 8 = 20 - 8 \rightarrow 4x = 12 \rightarrow$ Divide both sides by 4:
$4x = 12 \rightarrow \frac{4x}{4} = \frac{12}{4} \rightarrow x = 3$
Let's check this solution by substituting the value of 3 for x in the original equation: $x = 3 \rightarrow 2x + 8 = 20 - 2x \rightarrow 2(3) + 8 = 20 - 2(3) \rightarrow 6 + 8 = 20 - 6 \rightarrow 14 = 14$, The answer $x = 3$ is correct.

Find more at

System of Equations

☆ A system of equations contains two equations and two variables. For example, consider the system of equations: $x - y = 1$ and $x + y = 5$

☆ The easiest way to solve a system of equations is using the elimination method. The elimination method uses the addition property of equality. You can add the same value to each side of an equation.

☆ For the first equation above, you can add $x + y$ to the left side and 5 to the right side of the first equation: $x - y + (x + y) = 1 + 5$. Now, if you simplify, you get: $x - y + (x + y) = 1 + 5 \to 2x = 6 \to x = 3$. Now, substitute 3 for the x in the first equation: $3 - y = 1$. By solving this equation, $y = 2$

Example:

Example 1. What is the value of $x + y$ in this system of equations?

$$\begin{cases} x + 2y = 10 \\ 2x - y = -15 \end{cases}$$

Solution: Solving a System of Equations by Elimination:
Multiply the first equation by (-2), then add it to the second equation.

$$\begin{array}{l} -2(x + 2y = 10) \\ \underline{2x - y = -15} \end{array} \Rightarrow \begin{array}{l} -2x - 4y = -20 \\ 2x - y = -15 \end{array} \Rightarrow (-2x) + 2x - 4y - y = -20 - 15 \Rightarrow -5y = $$

$-35 \Rightarrow y = 7$

Plug in the value of y into one of the equations and solve for x.
$x + 2y = 10 \Rightarrow x + 2(7) = 10 \Rightarrow x + 14 = 10 \Rightarrow x = -4$
Thus, $x + y = -4 + 7 = 3$

 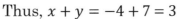

bit.ly/3mPGO6k

Find more at

Day 10: Practices

✎ Solve each equation. (One–Step Equations)

1) $x + 6 = 3 \rightarrow x =$ ___-3___

2) $4 = 12 - x \rightarrow x =$ ___

3) $-3 = 8 + x \rightarrow x =$ ___

4) $x - 2 = -9 \rightarrow x =$ ___

5) $-15 = x + 6 \rightarrow x =$ ___

6) $10 - x = -2 \rightarrow x =$ ___

7) $18 - x = -9 \rightarrow x =$ ___

8) $-4 + x = 28 \rightarrow x =$ ___

9) $11 - x = -7 \rightarrow x =$ ___

10) $26 - x = -7 \rightarrow x =$ ___

✎ Solve each equation. (Multi–Step Equations)

11) $8(x + 4) = 16 \rightarrow x =$ ___

12) $-6(6 - x) = 12 \rightarrow x =$ ___

13) $5 = -5(x + 2) \rightarrow x =$ ___

14) $-14 = 2(4 + x) \rightarrow x =$ ___

15) $4(x + 2) = -12, x =$ ___

16) $-6(3 + 2x) = 30, x =$ ___

17) $-3(4 - x) = 12, x =$ ___

18) $-4(6 - x) = 16, x =$ ___

✎ Solve each system of equations.

19) $\begin{cases} x + 6y = 32 \\ x + 3y = 17 \end{cases}$ $x =$ ___2___ $y =$ ___5___

20) $\begin{cases} 3x + y = 15 \\ x + 2y = 10 \end{cases}$ $x =$ ___4___ $y =$ ___3___

(handwritten work:)
$x + 6 = 32$
$-2x - 6y = -34$
$-x = -2$
$\frac{-x}{-1} = \frac{-2}{-1}$
$x = 2$
$x + 3y = 17$
-2
$\frac{3y}{3} = \frac{15}{3}$
$y = 5$

$3x + y = 15$
$-3x - 6y = -30$
$\frac{-5y}{-5} = \frac{-15}{-5}$
$y = 3$
$x + 2(3) = 10$
$x + 6 = 10$
$-6 \quad -6$
$x = 4$

Effortless Math Education

Day 10: Answers

1) -3

2) 8

3) -11

4) -7

5) -21

6) 12

7) 27

8) 32

9) 18

10) 33

11) -2

12) 8

13) -3

14) -11

15) -5

16) -4

17) 8

18) 10

19) $x = 2, y = 5$

20) $x = 4, y = 3$

Effortless
Math
Education

DAY 11 Inequalities

Math topics that you'll learn in this chapter:

1. Graphing Single–Variable Inequalities

2. One-Step Inequalities

3. Multi-Step Inequalities

73

Graphing Single–Variable Inequalities

☆ An inequality compares two expressions using an inequality sign.

☆ Inequality signs are: "less than" <, "greater than" >, "less than or equal to" ≤, and "greater than or equal to" ≥.

☆ To graph a single–variable inequality, find the value of the inequality on the number line.

☆ For less than (<) or greater than (>) draw an open circle on the value of the variable. If there is an equal sign too, then use a filled circle.

☆ Draw an arrow to the right for greater or to the left for less than.

Examples:

Example 1. Draw a graph for this inequality. $x > 4$

Solution: Since the variable is greater than 4, then we need to find 4 in the number line and draw an open circle on it. Then, draw an arrow to the right.

Example 2. Graph this inequality. $x \leq -1$.

Solution: Since the variable is less than or equal to −1, then we need to find −1 on the number line and draw a filled circle on it. Then, draw an arrow to the left.

bit.ly/3aJ4GGo
Find more at

One–Step Inequalities

☆ An inequality compares two expressions using an inequality sign.

☆ Inequality signs are: "less than" <, "greater than" >, "less than or equal to" ≤, and "greater than or equal to" ≥.

☆ You only need to perform one Math operation to solve the one-step inequalities.

☆ To solve one-step inequalities, find the inverse (opposite) operation is being performed.

☆ For dividing or multiplying both sides by negative numbers, flip the direction of the inequality sign.

Examples:

Example 1. Solve. $2x \leq -8$

Solution: 2 is multiplied to x. Divide both sides by 2.
Then: $2x \leq -8 \rightarrow \frac{2x}{2} \leq \frac{-8}{2} \rightarrow x \leq -4$

Example 2. Solve. $-4x \leq 16$ $x \geq -4$

Solution: -4 is multiplied to x. Divide both sides by -4. Remember when dividing or multiplying both sides of an inequality by negative numbers, flip the direction of the inequality sign.
Then: $-4x \leq 16 \rightarrow \frac{-4x}{-4} \geq \frac{16}{-4} \rightarrow x \geq -4$

Example 3. Solve this inequality for x. $x + 7 \geq 6$

Solution: The inverse (opposite) operation of addition is subtraction. In this inequality, 7 is added to x. To isolate x we need to subtract 7 from both sides of the inequality.
Then: $x + 7 \geq 6 \rightarrow x + 7 - 7 \geq 6 - 7 \rightarrow x \geq -1$. The solution is: $x \geq -1$

Multi–Step Inequalities

☆ To solve a multi-step inequality, combine "like" terms on one side.

☆ Bring variables to one side by adding or subtracting.

☆ Isolate the variable.

☆ Simplify using the inverse of addition or subtraction.

☆ Simplify further by using the inverse of multiplication or division.

☆ For dividing or multiplying both sides by negative numbers, flip the direction of the inequality sign.

Examples:

Example 1. Solve this inequality. $2x - 2 \le 12$

Solution: In this inequality, 2 is subtracted from $2x$. The inverse of subtraction is addition. Add 2 to both sides of the inequality:

$2x - 2 + 2 \le 12 + 2 \rightarrow 2x \le 14$

Now, divide both sides by 2. Then: $2x \le 14 \rightarrow \frac{2x}{2} \le \frac{14}{2} \rightarrow x \le 7$

The solution of this inequality is $x \le 7$.

Example 2. Solve this inequality. $3x + 10 < 13$

Solution: First, subtract 10 from both sides: $3x + 10 - 10 < 13 - 10$

Then simplify: $3x + 10 - 10 < 13 - 10 \rightarrow 3x < 3$

Now divide both sides by 3: $\frac{3x}{3} < \frac{3}{3} \rightarrow x < 1$

Example 3. Solve this inequality. $-7x + 5 \ge 12$

Solution: First, subtract 5 from both sides:

$-7x + 5 - 5 \ge 12 - 5 \rightarrow -7x \ge 7$

Divide both sides by -7. Remember that you need to flip the direction of inequality sign. $-7x \ge 7 \rightarrow \frac{-7x}{-7} \le \frac{7}{-7} \rightarrow x \le -1$

bit.ly/2WK1xOr

Find more at

Day 11: Practices

✍ Draw a graph for each inequality.

1) $x \leq -3$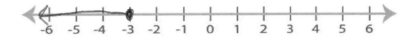

2) $x > -5$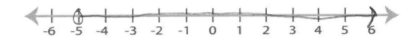

✍ Solve each inequality and graph it.

3) $x - 2 \geq -2$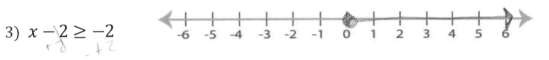

$x \geq 0$

4) $2x - 3 < 9$

$\frac{2x}{2} < \frac{12}{2}$ $x < 6$

✍ Solve each inequality.

5) $x + 10 > 4$ $x > -6$

6) $x + 6 > 5$ $x > -1$

7) $-12 + 2x \leq 26$ $2x \leq$

8) $-2 + 4x \leq 14$

9) $6 + 4x \leq 18$

10) $4(x + 3) \geq -12$

11) $2(6 + x) \geq -12$

12) $3(x - 5) < -6$

13) $10 + 5x < -15$

14) $6(6 + x) \geq -18$

Day 11: Answers

1) $x \le -3$

2) $x > -5$

3) $x \ge 0$

4) $x < 6$

5) $x > -6$

6) $x > -1$

7) $x \le 19$

8) $x \le 4$

9) $x \le 3$

10) $x \ge -6$

11) $x \ge -12$

12) $x < 3$

13) $x < -5$

14) $x \ge -9$

Effortless Math Education

DAY 12 Lines and Slope

Math topics that you'll learn in this chapter:

1. Finding Slope
2. Graphing Lines Using Slope–Intercept Form
3. Writing Linear Equations

79

Finding Slope

☆ The slope of a line represents the direction of a line on the coordinate plane.

☆ A coordinate plane contains two perpendicular number lines. The horizontal line is x and the vertical line is y. The point at which the two axes intersect is called the origin. An ordered pair (x, y) shows the location of a point.

☆ A line on a coordinate plane can be drawn by connecting two points.

☆ To find the slope of a line, we need the equation of the line or two points on the line.

☆ The slope of a line with two points A (x_1, y_1) and B (x_2, y_2) can be found by using this formula: $\frac{y_2 - y_1}{x_2 - x_1} = \frac{rise}{run}$

☆ The equation of a line is typically written as $y = mx + b$ where m is the slope and b is the y-intercept.

Examples:

Example 1. Find the slope of the line through these two points:

$A(1, -8)$ and $B(3, 4)$.

Solution: Slope $= \frac{y_2 - y_1}{x_2 - x_1}$. Let (x_1, y_1) be A$(1, -8)$ and (x_2, y_2) be $B(3, 4)$.

(Remember, you can choose any point for (x_1, y_1) and (x_2, y_2)).

Then: slope $= \frac{y_2 - y_1}{x_2 - x_1} = \frac{4 - (-8)}{3 - 1} = \frac{12}{2} = 6$, The slope of the line through these two points is 6.

Example 2. Find the slope of the line with equation $y = -5x + 14$

Solution: When the equation of a line is written in the form of $y = mx + b$, the slope is m. In this line: $y = -5x + 14$, the slope is -5.

Graphing Lines Using Slope–Intercept Form

☆ Slope–intercept form of a line: given the slope **m** and the **y**-intercept (the intersection of the line and y-axis) **b**, then the equation of the line is:

$$y = mx + b$$

☆ To draw the graph of a linear equation in a slope-intercept form on the xy coordinate plane, find two points on the line by plugging two values for x and calculating the values of y.

☆ You can also use the slope (m) and one point to graph the line.

Example:

Example 1. Sketch the graph of $y = 3x - 9$.

Solution: To graph this line, we need to find two points. When x is zero the value of y is -9. And when x is 3 the value of y is 0.

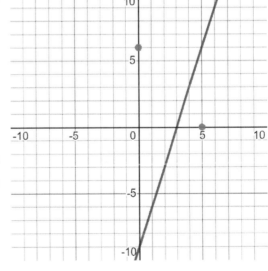

$$x = 0 \rightarrow y = 3(0) - 9 = -9,$$
$$y = 0 \rightarrow 0 = 3x - 9 \rightarrow x = 3$$

Now, we have two points:
$(0, -9)$ and $(3, 0)$.
Find the points on the coordinate plane and graph the line. Remember that the slope of the line is 3.

Writing Linear Equations

✰ The equation of a line in slope-intercept form: $y = mx + b$

✰ To write the equation of a line, first identify the slope.

✰ Find the $y-$intercept. This can be done by substituting the slope and the coordinates of a point (x, y) on the line.

Examples:

Example 1. What is the equation of the line that passes through $(5, -4)$ and has a slope of 3?

Solution: The general slope-intercept form of the equation of a line is $y = mx + b$, where m is the slope and b is the $y-$intercept. By substitution of the given point and given slope: $y = mx + b \rightarrow -4 = (3)(5) + b$. So, $b = -4 - 15 = -19$, and the required equation of the line is: $y = 3x - 19$

Example 2. Write the equation of the line through two points $A(5, 3)$ and $B(-1, 9)$.

Solution: First, find the slope: Slop $= \frac{y_2 - y_1}{x_2 - x_1} = \frac{9 - 3}{-1 - 5} = \frac{6}{-6} = -1 \rightarrow m = -1$

To find the value of b, use either points and plug in the values of x and y in the equation. The answer will be the same: $y = -x + b$. Let's check both points.
Then: $(5, 3) \rightarrow y = mx + b \rightarrow 3 = -1(5) + b \rightarrow b = 8$
$(-1, 9) \rightarrow y = mx + b \rightarrow 9 = -1(-1) + b \rightarrow b = 8$.
The equation of the line is: $y = -x + 8$

bit.ly/3nMKcAl

Find more at

Day 12: Practices

✏ Find the slope of each line.

1) $y = -x - 6$

2) $y = 6x + 3$

3) $y = -5x - 12$

4) $Line\ through\ (4, 3)\ and\ (3, 0)$

5) $Line\ through\ (1, 2)\ and\ (-3, 6)$

6) $Line\ through\ (-3, -5)\ and\ (-5, 9)$

✏ Sketch the graph of each line. (Using Slope–Intercept Form)

7) $y = x + 2$

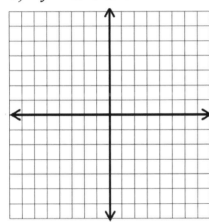

8) $y = 2x - 5$

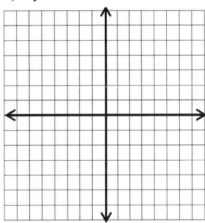

✏ Solve.

9) What is the equation of a line with slope 9 and intercept 12? _____

10) What is the equation of a line with slope 7 and passes through point $(1, 5)$?

_____

11) What is the equation of a line with slope -3 and passes through point $(-2, 7)$? _____

12) The slope of a line is -2 and it passes through point $(-6, 2)$. What is the equation of the line? _____

Day 12: Answers

1) -1

2) 6

3) -5

7) $y = x + 4$

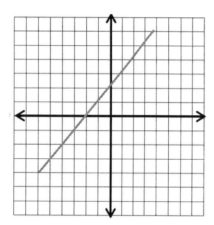

4) 3

5) -1

6) -7

8) $y = 2x - 5$

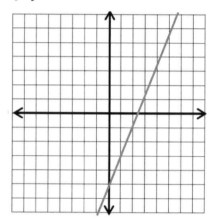

9) $y = 9x + 12$

10) $y = 7x - 2$

11) $y = -3x + 1$

12) $y = -2x - 10$

Effortless Math Education

DAY 13 Midpoint and Distance of two points

Math topics that you'll learn in this chapter:

1. Finding Midpoint
2. Finding Distance of Two Points
3. Graphing Linear Inequalities

85

Finding Midpoint

☆ The middle of a line segment is its midpoint.

☆ The Midpoint of two endpoints A (x_1, y_1) and B (x_2, y_2) can be found using this formula: M $\left(\frac{x_1+x_2}{2}, \frac{y_1+y_2}{2}\right)$

Examples:

Example 1. Find the midpoint of the line segment with the given endpoints. $(4, -6), (8, 10)$

Solution: Midpoint $= \left(\frac{x_1+x_2}{2}, \frac{y_1+y_2}{2}\right) \rightarrow (x_1, y_1) = (4, -6)$ and $(x_2, y_2) = (8, 10)$
Midpoint $= \left(\frac{4+8}{2}, \frac{-6+10}{2}\right) \rightarrow \left(\frac{12}{2}, \frac{4}{2}\right) \rightarrow M(6, 2)$

Example 2. Find the midpoint of the line segment with the given endpoints. $(-4, 5), (8, -9)$

Solution: Midpoint $= \left(\frac{x_1+x_2}{2}, \frac{y_1+y_2}{2}\right) \rightarrow (x_1, y_1) = (-4, 5)$ and $(x_2, y_2) = (8, -9)$
Midpoint $= \left(\frac{-4+8}{2}, \frac{5+(-9)}{2}\right) \rightarrow \left(\frac{4}{2}, \frac{-4}{2}\right) \rightarrow M(2, -2)$

Example 3. Find the midpoint of the line segment with the given endpoints. $(9, -6), (3, 10)$

Solution: Midpoint $= \left(\frac{x_1+x_2}{2}, \frac{y_1+y_2}{2}\right) \rightarrow (x_1, y_1) = (9, -6)$ and $(x_2, y_2) = (3, 10)$
Midpoint $= \left(\frac{9+3}{2}, \frac{-6+10}{2}\right) \rightarrow \left(\frac{12}{2}, \frac{4}{2}\right) \rightarrow M(6, 2)$

Example 4. Find the midpoint of the line segment with the given endpoints. $(4, 1), (8, -7)$

Solution: Midpoint $= \left(\frac{x_1+x_2}{2}, \frac{y_1+y_2}{2}\right) \rightarrow (x_1, y_1) = (4, \ 1)$ and $(x_2, y_2) = (8, -7)$
Midpoint $= \left(\frac{4+8}{2}, \frac{1-7}{2}\right) \rightarrow \left(\frac{12}{2}, \frac{-6}{2}\right) \rightarrow M(6, -3)$

Finding Distance of Two Points

☆ Use the following formula to find the distance of two points with the coordinates A (x_1, y_1) and B (x_2, y_2):

$$d = \sqrt{(x_2 - x_1)^2 + (y_2 - y_1)^2}$$

Examples:

Example 1. Find the distance between $(3, 3)$ and $(6, -1)$ on the coordinate plane.

Solution: Use distance of two point's formula: $d = \sqrt{(x_2 - x_1)^2 + (y_2 - y_1)^2}$

$(x_1, y_1) = (3, 3)$ and $(x_2, y_2) = (6, -1)$. Then: $d = \sqrt{(x_2 - x_1)^2 + (y_2 - y_1)^2} \rightarrow$

$= \sqrt{(6 - 3)^2 + (-1 - 3)^2} = \sqrt{(3)^2 + (-4)^2} = \sqrt{9 + 16} = \sqrt{25} = 5$

Then: $d = 5$

Example 2. Find the distance of two points $(2, 6)$ and $(10, -9)$.

Solution: Use distance of two point's formula: $d = \sqrt{(x_2 - x_1)^2 + (y_2 - y_1)^2}$

$(x_1, y_1) = (2, 6)$, and $(x_2, y_2) = (10, -9)$

Then: $= \sqrt{(x_2 - x_1)^2 + (y_2 - y_1)^2} \rightarrow d = \sqrt{(10 - 2)^2 + (-9 - 6)^2} = \sqrt{(8)^2 + (-15)^2} =$

$\sqrt{64 + 225} = \sqrt{289} = 17$. Then: $d = 17$

Example 3. Find the distance between $(-2, 8)$ and $(-6, 8)$.

Solution: Use distance of two point's formula: $d = \sqrt{(x_2 - x_1)^2 + (y_2 - y_1)^2}$

$(x_1, y_1) = (-2, 8)$ and $(x_2, y_2) = (-6, 8)$. Then: $d = \sqrt{(x_2 - x_1)^2 + (y_2 - y_1)^2}$

$d = \sqrt{(-6 - (-2))^2 + (8 - 8)^2} = \sqrt{(-4)^2 + (0)^2} = \sqrt{16} = 4$. Then: $d = 4$

Graphing Linear Inequalities

✰ To graph a linear inequality, first draw a graph of the "equals" line.

✰ Use a dash line for less than ($<$) and greater than ($>$) signs and a solid line for less than and equal to ($\leq$) and greater than and equal to ($\geq$).

✰ Choose a testing point. (it can be any point on both sides of the line.)

✰ Put the value of (x, y) of that point in the inequality. If that works, that part of the line is the solution. If the values don't work, then the other part of the line is the solution.

Example:

Example 1. Sketch the graph of inequality: $y < 3x + 5$

Solution: To draw the graph of $y < 3x + 5$, you first need to graph the line:

$y < 3x + 5$

Since there is a less than ($<$) sign, draw a dash line.

The slope is 3 and y −intercept is 5.

Then, choose a testing point and substitute the value of x and y from that point into the inequality. The easiest point to test is the origin: $(0, 0)$

$(0,0) \rightarrow y < 3x + 5 \rightarrow 0 < 3(0) + 5 \rightarrow 0 < 5$

This is correct! 0 is less than 5. So, this part of the line (on the right side) is the solution of this inequality.

Day 13: Practices

 **Sketch the graph of each linear inequality.**

1) $y > x - 6$

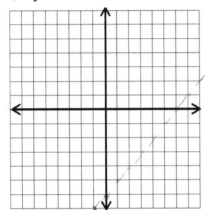

2) $y < -2x + 5$

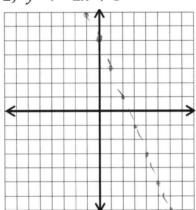

 Find the midpoint of the line segment with the given endpoints.

$$\frac{2+4}{2} \mid \frac{3+5}{2}$$

3) $(2,3), (4,5)$ $\quad \frac{6}{2} \mid \frac{8}{2} \ (3,4)$

4) $(4,5), (6,9)$

5) $(6,1), (4,5)$

6) $(5,8), (3,6)$

7) $(6,-3), (-4,9)$

8) $(2,-5), (4,1)$

9) $(5,4), (-3,2)$

10) $(-4,10), (6,-8)$

 Find the distance between each pair of points.

$$\sqrt{(3-5)^2 + (21-6)^2}$$

11) $(-5,6), (3,21)$

12) $(-1,9), (-5,6)$

13) $(5,9), (-11,-3)$

14) $(0,-2), (5,10)$

Effortless Math Education

www.EffortlessMath.com

89

Day 13: Answers

1) $y > x - 6$

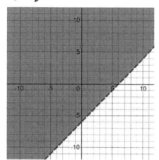

2) $y < -2x + 5$

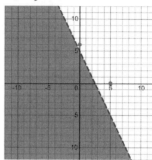

3) $(3, 4)$

4) $(5, 7)$

5) $(5, 3)$

6) $(4, 7)$

7) $(1, 3)$

8) $(3, -2)$

9) $(1, 3)$

10) $(1, 1)$

11) 17

12) 5

13) 20

14) 13

Effortless Math Education

 **DAY 14 Polynomials**

Math topics that you'll learn in this chapter:

1. Simplifying Polynomials
2. Adding and Subtracting Polynomials
3. Multiplying Monomials
4. Multiplying and Dividing Monomials

 91

Simplifying Polynomials

☆ To simplify Polynomials, find "like" terms. (they have same variables with same power).

☆ Use "FOIL". (First–Out–In–Last) for binomials:

$$(x + a)(x + b) = x^2 + (b + a)x + ab$$

☆ Add or Subtract "like" terms using order of operation.

Examples:

Example 1. Simplify this expression. $x(2x + 5) - 3x =$

Solution: Use Distributive Property: $x(2x + 5) = 2x^2 + 5x$

Now, combine like terms: $x(2x + 5) - 3x = 2x^2 + 5x - 3x = 2x^2 + 2x$

Example 2. Simplify this expression. $(x + 4)(x + 3) =$

Solution: First, apply the FOIL method: $(a + b)(c + d) = ac + ad + bc + bd$

$(x + 4)(x + 3) = x^2 + 4x + 3x + 12$

Now combine like terms: $x^2 + 4x + 3x + 12 = x^2 + 7x + 12$

Example 3. Simplify this expression. $3x(x - 4) - 2x^2 + 5x =$

Solution: Use Distributive Property: $3x(x - 4) = 3x^2 - 12x$

Then: $3x(x - 4) - 2x^2 + 5x = 3x^2 - 12x - 2x^2 + 5x$

Now combine like terms: $3x^2 - 2x^2 = x^2$, and $-12x + 5x = -7x$

The simplified form of the expression:

$3x^2 - 12x - 2x^2 + 5x = x^2 - 7x$

bit.ly/3rnAcj8

Find more at

Adding and Subtracting Polynomials

☆ Adding polynomials is just a matter of combining like terms, with some order of operations considerations thrown in.

☆ Be careful with the minus signs, and don't confuse addition and multiplication!

☆ For subtracting polynomials, sometimes you need to use the Distributive Property: $a(b + c) = ab + ac$, $a(b - c) = ab - ac$

Examples:

Example 1. Simplify the expressions. $(2x^2 - 2x^3) - (x^3 - 5x^2) =$

Solution: First, use Distributive Property:
$-(x^3 - 5x^2) = -x^3 + 5x^2$
$\rightarrow (2x^2 - 2x^3) - (x^3 - 5x^2) = 2x^2 - 2x^3 - x^3 + 5x^2$
Now combine like terms: $-x^3 - 2x^3 = -3x^3$ and $2x^2 + 5x^2 = 7x^2$
Then: $(2x^2 - 2x^3) - (x^3 - 5x^2) = 2x^2 - 2x^3 - x^3 + 5x^2 = -3x^3 + 7x^2$

Example 2. Add expressions. $(4x^3 - 7) + (5x^3 - 2x^2) =$

Solution: Remove parentheses:
$(4x^3 - 7) + (5x^3 - 2x^2) = 4x^3 - 7 + 5x^3 - 2x^2$
Now combine like terms: $4x^3 - 7 + 5x^3 - 2x^2 = 9x^3 - 2x^2 - 7$

Example 3. Simplify the expressions. $(-3x^2 - 4x^3) - (6x^2 + 2x^3) =$

Solution: First, use Distributive Property: $-(6x^2 + 2x^3) = -6x^2 - 2x^3 \rightarrow$
$(-3x^2 - 4x^3) - (6x^2 + 2x^3) = -3x^2 - 4x^3 - 6x^2 - 2x^3$
Now combine like terms and write in standard form:
$-3x^2 - 4x^3 - 6x^2 - 2x^3 = -6x^3 - 9x^2$

Multiplying Monomials

☆ A monomial is a polynomial with just one term: Examples: $2x$ or $7y^2$.

☆ When you multiply monomials, first multiply the coefficients (a number placed before and multiplying the variable) and then multiply the variables using multiplication property of exponents.

$$x^a \times x^b = x^{a+b}$$

Examples:

Example 1. Multiply expressions. $3xy^4 \times 5x^4y^3$

Solution: Find the same variables and use multiplication property of exponents: $x^a \times x^b = x^{a+b}$
$x \times x^4 = x^{1+4} = x^5$ and $y^4 \times y^3 = y^{4+3} = y^7$
Then, multiply coefficients and variables: $3xy^4 \times 5x^4y^3 = 15x^5y^7$

Example 2. Multiply expressions. $3a^4b^7 \times 6a^5b^5 =$

Solution: Use the multiplication property of exponents: $x^a \times x^b = x^{a+b}$
$a^4 \times a^5 = a^{4+5} = a^9$ and $b^7 \times b^5 = b^{7+5} = b^{12}$
Then: $3a^3b^8 \times 6a^6b^4 = 18a^9b^{12}$

Example 3. Multiply. $5x^3y^5z^3 \times 7x^5y^8z^5$

Solution: Use the multiplication property of exponents: $x^a \times x^b = x^{a+b}$
$x^3 \times x^5 = x^{3+5} = x^8$, $y^5 \times y^8 = y^{5+8} = y^{13}$ and $z^3 \times z^5 = z^{3+5} = z^8$
Then: $5x^3y^5z^3 \times 7x^5y^8z^5 = 35x^8y^{13}z^8$

Example 4. Simplify. $\left(-9a^8b^5\right)\left(4a^9b^6\right) =$

Solution: Use the multiplication property of exponents: $x^a \times x^b = x^{a+b}$
$a^8 \times a^9 = a^{8+9} = a^{17}$ and $b^5 \times b^6 = b^{5+6} = b^{11}$
Then: $\left(-9a^8b^5\right)\left(4a^9b^6\right) = -36a^{17}b^{11}$

bit.ly/2KLVoP8
Find more at

Multiplying and Dividing Monomials

☆ When you divide or multiply two monomials, you need to divide or multiply their coefficients and then divide or multiply their variables.

☆ In case of exponents with the same base, for Division, subtract their powers, for Multiplication, add their powers.

☆ Exponent's Multiplication and Division rules:

$$x^a \times x^b = x^{a+b}, \qquad \frac{x^a}{x^b} = x^{a-b}$$

Examples:

Example 1. Multiply expressions. $(7x^8)(6x^5) =$

Solution: Use multiplication property of exponents:
$x^a \times x^b = x^{a+b} \rightarrow x^8 \times x^5 = x^{13}$
Then: $(7x^8)(6x^5) = 42x^{13}$

Example 2. Divide expressions. $\frac{32x^5y^7}{4x^2y^2} =$

Solution: Use division property of exponents:
$\frac{x^a}{x^b} = x^{a-b} \rightarrow \frac{x^5}{x^2} = x^{5-2} = x^3$ and $\frac{y^7}{y^2} = y^{7-2} = y^5$
Then: $\frac{32x^5y^7}{4x^2y^2} = 8x^3y^5$

Example 3. Divide expressions. $\frac{54a^7b^8}{9a^3b^4}$ $6a^4b^4$

Solution: Use division property of exponents:
$\frac{x^a}{x^b} = x^{a-b} \rightarrow \frac{a^7}{a^3} = a^{7-3} = a^4$ and $\frac{b^8}{b^4} = b^{8-4} = b^4$
Then: $\frac{54a^7b^8}{9a^3b^4} = 6a^4b^4$

Day 14: Practices

✍ Simplify each polynomial.

1) $5(3x + 4) =$

2) $-3(2x - 7) =$

3) $x(4x + 5) + 8x =$

4) $6x(x + 3) + 5x =$

5) $8(2x + 3) - 5x =$

6) $x(3x - 4) + 3x^2 - 6 =$

7) $x^2 - 5 - 3x(x + 8) =$

8) $2x^2 + 5 - 7x(2x + 5) =$

✍ Add or subtract polynomials.

9) $(x^2 + 6) + (2x^2 - 5) =$

10) $(3x^2 - 6x) - (x^2 + 8x) =$

11) $(5x^3 - 3x^2) + (3x^3 - 5x^2) =$

12) $(6x^3 - 7x) - (5x^3 - 3x) =$

13) $(7x^3 + 3x) - (5x^3 - 4x) =$

14) $(7x^3 - 5x) - (3x^3 + 5x) =$

✍ Find the products. (Multiplying Monomials)

15) $2x^2 \times 8x^3 =$

16) $5x^5 \times 4x^3 =$

17) $-4a^4b \times 2ab^3 =$

18) $-3a^4bc \times 6a^2b^4 =$

19) $-6a^3bc \times 5a^4b^3 =$

20) $-5x^6y^3 \times (-7xy^2) =$

✍ Simplify each expression. (Multiplying and Dividing Monomials)

21) $(5x^2y^2)(3x^4y^3) =$

22) $(10x^8y^5)(3x^5y^7) =$

23) $\dfrac{36x^4y^7}{3x^2y} =$

24) $\dfrac{63x^{13}y^{10}}{9x^8y^6} =$

Effortless Math Education

Day 14: Answers

1) $15x + 20$

2) $-6x + 21$

3) $4x^2 + 13x$

4) $6x^2 + 23x$

5) $11x + 24$

6) $6x^2 - 4x - 6$

7) $-2x^2 - 24x - 5$

8) $-12x^2 - 35x + 5$

9) $3x^2 + 1$

10) $2x^2 - 14x$

11) $8x^3 - 8x^2$

12) $x^3 - 4x$

13) $2x^3 + 7x$

14) $4x^3 - 10x$

15) $16x^5$

16) $20x^8$

17) $-8a^5b^4$

18) $-18a^6b^5c$

19) $-30a^7b^4c$

20) $35x^7y^5$

21) $15x^6y^5$

22) $30x^{13}y^{12}$

23) $12x^2y^6$

24) $7x^5y^4$

Effortless Math Education

DAY 15 Binomials and Trinomials

Math topics that you'll learn in this chapter:

1. Multiplying a Polynomial and a Monomial

2. Multiplying Binomials

3. Factoring Trinomials

99

Multiplying a Polynomial and a Monomial

☆ When multiplying monomials, use the product rule for exponents.

$$x^a \times x^b = x^{a+b}$$

☆ When multiplying a monomial by a polynomial, use the distributive property.

$$a \times (b + c) = a \times b + a \times c = ab + ac$$
$$a \times (b - c) = a \times b - a \times c = ab - ac$$

Examples:

Example 1. Multiply expressions. $3x(4x + 6)$

Solution: Use Distributive Property:

$3x(4x + 6) = 3x \times 4x + 3x \times 6 = 12x^2 + 18x$

Example 2. Multiply expressions. $x(2x^2 + 7y^2)$

Solution: Use Distributive Property:

$x(2x^2 + 7y^2) = x \times 2x^2 + x \times 7y^2 = 2x^3 + 7xy^2$

Example 3. Multiply. $-x(-3x^2 + 5x + 6)$

Solution: Use Distributive Property:

$-x(-3x^2 + 5x + 6) = (-x)(-3x^2) + (-x) \times (5x) + (-x) \times (6) =$

Now simplify:

$(-x)(-3x^2) + (-x) \times (5x) + (-x) \times (6) = 3x^3 - 5x^2 - 6x$

Multiplying Binomials

☆ A binomial is a polynomial that is the sum or the difference of two terms, each of which is a monomial.

☆ To multiply two binomials, use the "FOIL" method. (First–Out–In–Last)

$$(x + a)(x + b) = x \times x + x \times b + a \times x + a \times b = x^2 + bx + ax + ab$$

Examples:

Example 1. Multiply Binomials. $(x + 6)(x - 2) =$

Solution: Use "FOIL". (First–Out–In–Last):

$(x + 6)(x - 2) = x^2 - 2x + 6x - 12$

Then combine like terms: $x^2 - 2x + 6x - 12 = x^2 + 4x - 12$

Example 2. Multiply. $(x + 8)(x + 3) =$

Solution: Use "FOIL". (First–Out–In–Last):

$(x + 8)(x + 3) = x^2 + 3x + 8x + 24$

Then simplify: $x^2 + 3x + 8x + 24 = x^2 + 11x + 24$

Example 3. Multiply. $(x + 4)(x - 9) =$

Solution: Use "FOIL". (First–Out–In–Last):

$(x + 4)(x - 9) = x^2 - 9x + 4x - 36$

Then simplify: $x^2 - 9x + 4x - 36 = x^2 - 5x - 36$

Factoring Trinomials

To factor trinomials, you can use following methods:

★ "FOIL": $(x + a)(x + b) = x^2 + (b + a)x + ab$

★ "Difference of Squares":

$$a^2 - b^2 = (a + b)(a - b)$$
$$a^2 + 2ab + b^2 = (a + b)(a + b)$$
$$a^2 - 2ab + b^2 = (a - b)(a - b)$$

★ "Reverse FOIL": $x^2 + (b + a)x + ab = (x + a)(x + b)$

Examples:

Example 1. Factor this trinomial. $x^2 - 3x - 18$

Solution: Break the expression into groups: $(x^2 + 3x) + (-6x - 18)$

Now factor out x from $x^2 + 3x$: $x(x + 3)$, and factor out -6 from $-6x - 18$: $-6(x + 3)$

Then: $(x^2 + 3x) + (-6x - 18) = x(x + 3) - 6(x + 3)$, now factor out like term: $x + 3$

Then: $(x + 3)(x - 6)$

Example 2. Factor this trinomial. $x^2 + 12x + 32$

Solution: Break the expression into groups: $(x^2 + 4x) + (8x + 32)$
Now factor out x from $x^2 + 4x : x(x + 4)$, and factor out 8 from

$8x + 32: 8(x + 4)$; Then: $(x^2 + 4x) + (8x + 32) = x(x + 4) + 8(x + 4)$

Now factor out like term:

$(x + 4) \rightarrow (x + 4)(x + 8)$

bit.ly/38EpdJA
Find more at

Day 15: Practices

✎ Find each product. (Multiplying a Polynomial and a Monomial)

1) $2(4x - y) =$

2) $4(6x - 2y) =$

3) $2x(5x + y) =$

4) $5x(2x - 3y) =$

5) $x(x^2 - 3x) =$

6) $x(x^2 + 3x - 4) =$

7) $5x(3x^2 + 8x + 2) =$

8) $3x(2x^2 - 7x - 6) =$

✎ Find each product. (Multiplying Binomials)

9) $(-5)(x + 4) =$

10) $(x - 3)(x + 4) =$

11) $(x + 4)(x + 6) =$

12) $(x + 8)(x + 4) =$

13) $(x + 6)(x - 8) =$

14) $(x + 7)(x - 5) =$

15) $(x - 9)(x + 6) =$

16) $(x - 8)(x - 9) =$

✎ Factor each Trinomial.

17) $x^2 + 5x + 6 =$

18) $x^2 + 2x - 8 =$

19) $x^2 + 3x - 40 =$

20) $x^2 - 9x + 14 =$

21) $x^2 + 3x - 28 =$

22) $2x^2 - 7x + 12 =$

Day 15: Answers

1) $8x - 2y$

2) $24x - 8y$

3) $10x^2 + 2xy$

4) $10x^2 - 15xy$

5) $x^3 - 3x^2$

6) $x^3 + 3x^2 - 4x$

7) $15x^3 + 40x^2 + 10x$

8) $6x^3 - 21x^2 - 18x$

9) $-5x - 20$

10) $x^2 + x - 12$

11) $x^2 + 10x + 24$

12) $x^2 + 12x + 32$

13) $x^2 - 2x - 48$

14) $x^2 + 2x - 35$

15) $x^2 - 3x - 54$

16) $x^2 - 17x + 72$

17) $(x + 3)(x + 2)$

18) $(x + 4)(x - 2)$

19) $(x - 5)(x + 8)$

20) $(x - 7)(x - 2)$

21) $(x + 7)(x - 4)$

22) $(2x - 4)(x - 3$

Effortless Math Education

DAY 16 Geometry and Solid Figures

Math topics that you'll learn in this chapter:

1. The Pythagorean Theorem
2. Complementary and Supplementary angles
3. Parallel lines and Transversals
4. Triangles

105

The Pythagorean Theorem

☆ You can use the Pythagorean Theorem to find a missing side in a right triangle.

☆ In any right triangle: $a^2 + b^2 = c^2$

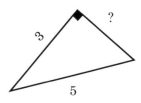

Examples:

Example 1. Right triangle ABC (not shown) has two legs of lengths $3\,cm$ (AB) and $4\,cm$ (AC). What is the length of the hypotenuse of the triangle (side BC)?

Solution: Use Pythagorean Theorem: $a^2 + b^2 = c^2$, $a = 3$, and $b = 4$

Then: $a^2 + b^2 = c^2 \rightarrow 3^2 + 4^2 = c^2 \rightarrow 9 + 16 = c^2 \rightarrow 25 = c^2 \rightarrow c = \sqrt{25} = 5$

The length of the hypotenuse is $5\,cm$.

Example 2. Find the hypotenuse of this triangle.

Solution: Use Pythagorean Theorem: $a^2 + b^2 = c^2$

Then: $a^2 + b^2 = c^2 \rightarrow 3^2 + b^2 = 5^2 \rightarrow 9 + b^2 = 25$

$b^2 = 16 \rightarrow c = \sqrt{16} = 4$

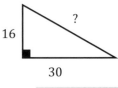

Example 3. Find the length of the missing side in this triangle.

Solution: Use Pythagorean Theorem: $a^2 + b^2 = c^2$

Then: $a^2 + b^2 = c^2 \rightarrow 30^2 + 16^2 = c^2 \rightarrow 900 + 256 = c^2 \rightarrow$

$c^2 = 1{,}156 \rightarrow c = \sqrt{1{,}156} = 34$

Complementary and Supplementary angles

✩ Two angles with a sum of 90 degrees are called complementary angles.

✩ Two angles with a sum of 180 degrees are Supplementary angles.

Examples:

Example 1. Find the missing angle.

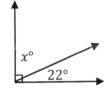

Solution: Notice that the two angles form a right angle. This means that the angles are complementary, and their sum is 90°. Then: $22° + x = 90° \rightarrow x = 90° - 22° = 68°$
The missing angle is 68 degrees. $x = 68°$

Example 2. Angles Q and S are supplementary. What is the measure of angle Q if angle S is 40 degrees?

Solution: Q and S are supplementary $\rightarrow Q + S = 180 \rightarrow Q + 40 = 180 \rightarrow$
$$Q = 180 - 40 = 140$$

Example 3. Angles x and y are complementary. What is the measure of angle x if angle y is 28 degrees?

Solution: Angles x and y are complementary $\rightarrow x + y = 90 \rightarrow x + 28 = 90 \rightarrow$
$$x = 90 - 28 = 62$$

Parallel lines and Transversals

☆ When a line (transversal) intersects two parallel lines in the same plane, eight angles are formed. In the following diagram, a transversal intersects two parallel lines. Angles 1, 3, 5, and 7 are congruent. Angles 2, 4, 6, and 8 are also congruent.

☆ In the following diagram, the following angles are supplementary angles (their sum is 180):

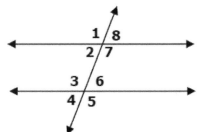

- ❖ Angles 1 and 8
- ❖ Angles 2 and 7
- ❖ Angles 3 and 6
- ❖ Angles 4 and 5

Example:

Example 1. In the following diagram, two parallel lines are cut by a transversal. What is the value of x?

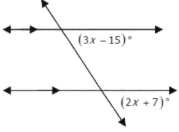

Solution: The two angles $3x - 15$ and $2x + 7$ are equivalent.

That is: $3x - 15 = 2x + 7$

Now, solve for x:

$3x - 15 + 15 = 2x + 7 + 15 \ \rightarrow 3x = 2x + 22 \rightarrow 3x - 2x = 2x + 22 - 2x \rightarrow$

$x = 22$

bit.ly/32Mcwu0
Find more at

Triangles

☆ In any triangle, the sum of all angles is 180 degrees.

☆ Area of a triangle $= \frac{1}{2} (base \times height)$

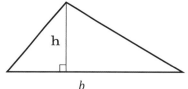

Examples:

Example 1. What is the area of this triangles?

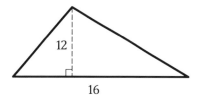

Solution: Use the area formula:
Area $= \frac{1}{2}(base \times height)$

$base = 16$ and $height = 12$, Then:
Area $= \frac{1}{2}(16 \times 12) = \frac{1}{2}(192) = 96$

Example 2. What is the area of this triangles?

Solution: Use the area formula:

Area $= \frac{1}{2}(base \times height)$
$base = 18$ and $height = 10$; Area $= \frac{1}{2}(18 \times 10) = \frac{180}{2} = 90$

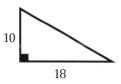

Example 3. What is the missing angle in this triangle?

Solution:

In any triangle, the sum of all angles is 180 degrees.
Let x be the missing angle.
Then: $50° + 85° + x = 180° \rightarrow 135° + x = 180° \rightarrow$
$x = 180° - 135° = 45°$
The missing angle is 45 degrees.

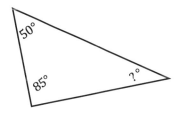

Day 16: Practices

✎ **Find the missing side?**

1)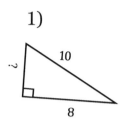

2)

3)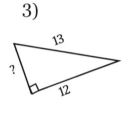

4)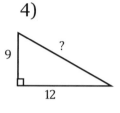

✎ **Find the measure of the unknown angle in each triangle.**

5) 6) 7) 8)
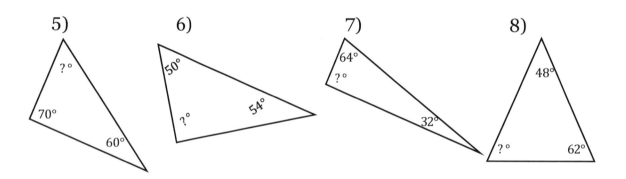

✎ **Find the area of each triangle.**

9) 10) 11) 12)
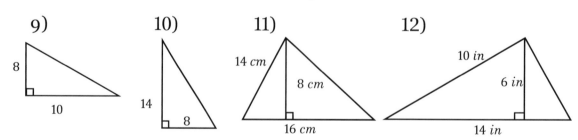

Day 16: Answers

1) 6

2) 13

3) 5

4) 15

5) 50

6) 76

7) 84

8) 70

9) 40

10) 56

11) 64 cm^2

12) 42 in^2

Effortless Math Education

DAY 17 Polygons and Circles

Math topics that you'll learn in this chapter:

1. Special Right Triangles

2. Polygons

3. Circles

113

Special Right Triangles

☆ A special right triangle is a triangle whose sides are in a particular ratio. Two special right triangles are $45° - 45° - 90°$ and $30° - 60° - 90°$ triangles.

☆ In a special $45° - 45° - 90°$ triangle, the three angles are $45°$, $45°$ and $90°$. The lengths of the sides of this triangle are in the ratio of $1:1:\sqrt{2}$.

☆ In a special triangle $30° - 60° - 90°$, the three angles are $30° - 60° - 90°$. The lengths of this triangle are in the ratio of $1:\sqrt{3}:2$.

Examples:

Example 1. Find the length of the hypotenuse of a right triangle if the length of the other two sides are both 4 inches.

Solution: this is a right triangle with two equal sides. Therefore, it must be a $45° - 45° - 90°$ triangle. Two equivalent sides are 4 inches. The ratio of sides: $x : x : x\sqrt{2}$

The length of the hypotenuse is $4\sqrt{2}$ inches. $x : x : x\sqrt{2} \rightarrow 4 : 4 : 4\sqrt{2}$

Example 2. The length of the hypotenuse of a right triangle is 6 inches. What are the lengths of the other two sides if one angle of the triangle is $30°$?

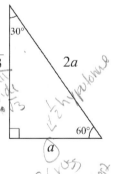

Solution: The hypotenuse is 6 inches and the triangle is a $30° - 60° - 90°$ triangle. Then, one side of the triangle is 3 (it's half the side of the hypotenuse) and the other side is $3\sqrt{3}$. (it's the smallest side times $\sqrt{3}$)

$x : x\sqrt{3} : 2x \rightarrow x = 3 \rightarrow x : x\sqrt{3} : 2x = 3 : 3\sqrt{3} : 6$

bit.ly/3xL9bJR

Find more at

Polygons

☆ The perimeter of a square = $4 \times side = 4s$

☆ The perimeter of a rectangle = $2(width + length)$

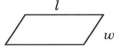

☆ The perimeter of trapezoid = $a + b + c + d$

☆ The perimeter of a regular hexagon = $6a$

☆ The perimeter of a parallelogram = $2(l + w)$

Examples:

Example 1. Find the perimeter of following regular hexagon.

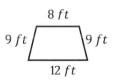

Solution: Since the hexagon is regular, all sides are equal.
Then, the perimeter of the hexagon = $6 \times (one\ side)$
The perimeter of the hexagon = $6 \times (one\ side) = 6 \times 9 = 54\ m$

Example 2. Find the perimeter of following trapezoid.

Solution: The perimeter of a trapezoid = $a + b + c + d$
The perimeter of the trapezoid = $8 + 9 + 9 + 12 = 38\ ft$

Circles

☆ In a circle, variable r is usually used for the radius and d for diameter.

☆ Area of a circle $= \pi r^2$ (π is about 3.14)

☆ Circumference of a circle $= 2\pi r$

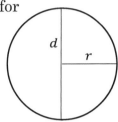

Examples:

Example 1. Find the area of this circle. ($\pi = 3.14$)

Solution:
Use area formula: Area $= \pi r^2$
$r = 8 \ in \rightarrow$ Area $= \pi(8)^2 = 64\pi$, $\pi = 3.14$
Then: Area $= 64 \times 3.14 = 200.96 \ in^2$

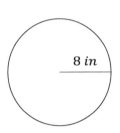

Example 2. Find the Circumference of this circle. ($\pi = 3.14$)

Solution:
Use Circumference formula: Circumference $= 2\pi r$
$r = 7 \ cm \rightarrow$ Circumference $= 2\pi(7) = 14\pi$
$\pi = 3.14$, Then: Circumference $= 14 \times 3.14 = 43.96 \ cm$

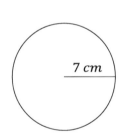

Example 3. Find the area of this circle.

Solution:
Use area formula: Area $= \pi r^2$
$r = 10 \ in$, Then: Area $= \pi(10)^2 = 100\pi$, $\pi = 3.14$
Area $= 100 \times 3.14 = 314 \ in^2$

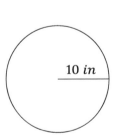

bit.ly/3nJdOP2
Find more at

Day 17: Practices

✎ **Find the value *of* x *and* y in each triangle.**

1) x = ___
   y = ___

2) x = ___
   y =

3) x = ___
   y = ___

4) x = ___
   y = ___

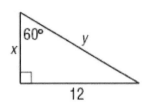 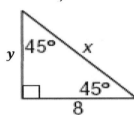 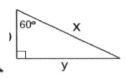 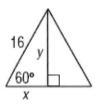

✎ **Find the perimeter or circumference of each shape.**

5)   6)   7)   8) *Regular hexagon*

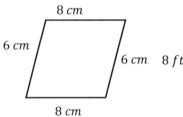 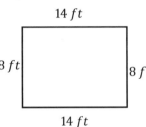 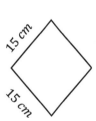 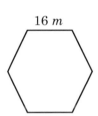

✎ **Find the Circumference and Area of each circle.** (π = 3.14)

9) _____   10) _____   11) _____   12) _____   13) _____

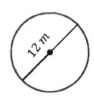

Effortless Math Education *www.EffortlessMath.com* ------------------ 117

Day 17: Answers

1) $x = 4\sqrt{3} \quad y = 8\sqrt{3}$

2) $x = 8\sqrt{2} \quad y = 8$

3) $x = 40 \quad y = 20\sqrt{3}$

4) $x = 8 \quad y = 8\sqrt{3}$

5) $28\ cm$

6) $44\ ft$

7) $60\ cm$

8) $96\ m$

9) $C = 69.08\ ft, A = 379.94\ in^2$

10) $C = 75.36\ m, A = 452.16\ m^2$

11) $C = 175.84\ cm, A = 2,461.76\ cm^2$

12) $C = 94.2\ miles, A = 706.5\ (miles)^2$

13) $C = 113.04\ ft, A = 1,017.36\ ft^2$

**Effortless
Math
Education**

DAY 18 Trapezoids and Cubes

Math topics that you'll learn in this chapter:

1. Trapezoids
2. Cubes
3. Rectangle Prisms
4. Cylinder

119

Trapezoids

☆ A quadrilateral with at least one pair of parallel sides is a trapezoid.

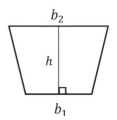

☆ Area of a trapezoid $= \frac{1}{2}h(b_1 + b_2)$

Examples:

Example 1. Calculate the area of this trapezoid.

Solution:

Use area formula: $A = \frac{1}{2}h(b_1 + b_2)$

$b_1 = 8\ cm$, $b_2 = 12\ cm$ and $h = 10\ cm$

Then: $A = \frac{1}{2}(10)(12 + 8) = 5(20) = 100\ cm^2$

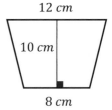

Example 2. Calculate the area of this trapezoid.

Solution:

Use area formula: $A = \frac{1}{2}h(b_1 + b_2)$

$b_1 = 12\ cm$, $b_2 = 18\ cm$ and $h = 16\ cm$

Then: $A = \frac{1}{2}(16)(12 + 18) = 8(30) = 240\ cm^2$

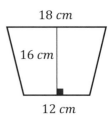

bit.ly/3hpKACJ

Find more at

Cubes

☆ A cube is a three-dimensional solid object bounded by six square sides.

☆ Volume is the measure of the amount of space inside of a solid figure, like a cube, ball, cylinder or pyramid.

☆ The volume of a cube $= (one\ side)^3$

☆ The surface area of a cube $= 6 \times (one\ side)^2$

Examples:

Example 1. Find the volume and surface area of this cube.

Solution: Use volume formula: $volume = (one\ side)^3$
Then: $volume = (one\ side)^3 = (4)^3 = 64\ cm^3$
Use surface area formula:
surface area of a cube: $6(one\ side)^2 = 6(4)^2 = 6(16) = 96\ cm^2$

Example 2. Find the volume and surface area of this cube.

Solution: Use volume formula: $volume = (one\ side)^3$
Then: $volume = (one\ side)^3 = (7)^3 = 343\ cm^3$
Use surface area formula:
surface area of a cube: $6(one\ side)^2 = 6(7)^2 = 6(49) = 294\ cm^2$

Example 3. Find the volume and surface area of this cube.

Solution: Use volume formula: $volume = (one\ side)^3$
Then: $volume = (one\ side)^3 = (9)^3 = 729\ m^3$
Use surface area formula:
surface area of a cube: $6(one\ side)^2 = 6(9)^2 = 6(81) = 486\ m^2$

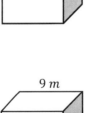

4 cm

7 cm

9 m

Rectangular Prisms

✪ A rectangular prism is a solid 3−dimensional object with six rectangular faces.

✪ The volume of a Rectangular prism = $Length \times Width \times Height$

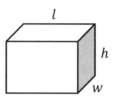

$Volume = l \times w \times h$
$Surface\ area = 2 \times (wh + lw + lh)$

Examples:

Example 1. Find the volume and surface area of this rectangular prism.

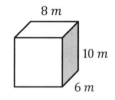

Solution: Use volume formula: $Volume = l \times w \times h$

Then: $Volume = 8 \times 6 \times 10 = 480\ m^3$

Use surface area formula: $Surface\ area = 2 \times (wh + lw + lh)$

Then: $Surface\ area = 2 \times \big((6 \times 10) + (8 \times 6) + (8 \times 10)\big)$

$= 2 \times (60 + 56 + 80) = 2 \times (196) = 392\ m^2$

Example 2. Find the volume and surface area of this rectangular prism.

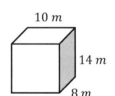

Solution: Use volume formula: $Volume = l \times w \times h$

Then: $Volume = 10 \times 8 \times 14 = 648\ m^3$

Use surface area formula: $Surface\ area = 2 \times (wh + lw + lh)$

Then: $Surface\ area = 2 \times \big((8 \times 14) + (10 \times 8) + (10 \times 14)\big)$

$= 2 \times (112 + 80 + 140) = 2 \times (332) = 664\ m^2$

bit.ly/3nKm2GT
Find more at

Cylinder

☆ A cylinder is a solid geometric figure with straight parallel sides and a circular or oval cross-section.

☆ Volume of a Cylinder $= \pi(radius)^2 \times height$, $\pi \approx 3.14$

☆ Surface area of a cylinder $= 2\pi r^2 + 2\pi rh$

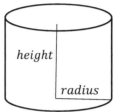

Examples:

Example 1. Find the volume and Surface area of the follow Cylinder.

Solution: Use volume formula:
$Volume = \pi(radius)^2 \times height$
Then: $Volume = \pi(4)^2 \times 12 = 16\pi \times 12 = 192\pi$
$\pi = 3.14$, then: $Volume = 192\pi = 192 \times 3.14 = 602.88 \ cm^3$
Use surface area formula: $Surface \ area = 2\pi r^2 + 2\pi rh$
Then: $2\pi(4)^2 + 2\pi(4)(12) = 2\pi(16) + 2\pi(48) = 32\pi + 96\pi = 128\pi$
$\pi = 3.14$, Then: $Surface \ area = 128 \times 3.14 = 401.92 \ cm^2$

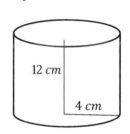

12 cm

4 cm

Example 2. Find the volume and Surface area of the follow Cylinder.

Solution: Use volume formula:
$Volume = \pi(radius)^2 \times height$
Then: $Volume = \pi(5)^2 \times 14 = 25\pi \times 14 = 350\pi$
$\pi = 3.14$, Then: $Volume = 350\pi = 1,099 \ cm^3$
Use surface area formula: $Surface \ area = 2\pi r^2 + 2\pi rh$
Then: $= 2\pi(5)^2 + 2\pi(5)(14) = 2\pi(25) + 2\pi(70) = 50\pi + 140\pi = 190\pi$
$\pi = 3.14$ then: $Surface \ area = 190 \times 3.14 = 596.6 \ cm^2$

14 cm

5 cm

Day 18: Practices

✎ Find the area of each trapezoid.

1)
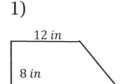
12 in
8 in
16 in

2)
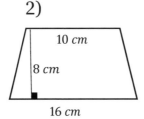
10 cm
8 cm
16 cm

3)
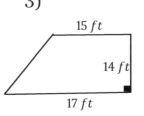
15 ft
14 ft
17 ft

4)
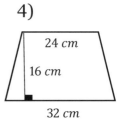
24 cm
16 cm
32 cm

✎ Find the volume of each cube.

5)
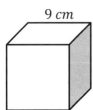
9 cm

6)
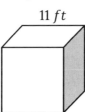
11 ft

7)
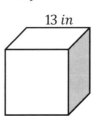
13 in

8)
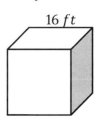
16 ft

✎ Find the volume of each Rectangular Prism.

9)
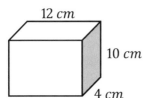
12 cm
10 cm
4 cm

10)
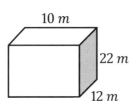
10 m
22 m
12 m

11)
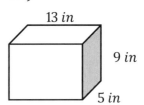
13 in
9 in
5 in

✎ Find the volume of each Cylinder. Round your answer to the nearest tenth. ($\pi = 3.14$)

12)
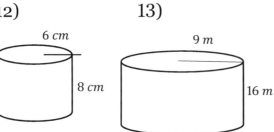
6 cm
8 cm

13)
9 m
16 m

14)
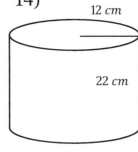
12 cm
22 cm

Effortless Math Education

Day 18: Answers

1) $112 \ in^2$

2) $104 \ cm^2$

3) $224 \ ft^2$

4) $448 \ cm^2$

5) $729 \ cm^3$

6) $1,331 \ ft^3$

7) $2,197 \ in^3$

8) $4,096 \ ft^3$

9) $480 \ cm^2$

10) $2,640 \ m^3$

11) $585 \ in^3$

12) $904.32 \ cm^3$

13) $4,069.44 \ m^3$

14) $9,947.52 \ cm^3$

**Effortless
Math
Education**

Math topics that you'll learn in this chapter:

1. Mean, Median, Mode, and Range of the Given Data
2. Pie Graph
3. Probability Problems
4. Permutations and Combinations

127

Mean, Median, Mode, and Range of the Given Data

☆ **Mean:** $\dfrac{sum\ of\ the\ data}{total\ number\ of\ data\ entires}$

☆ **Mode:** the value in the list that appears most often

☆ **Median:** is the middle number of a group of numbers arranged in order by size.

☆ **Range:** the difference of the largest value and smallest value in the list

Examples:

Example 1. What is the median of these numbers? $8, 13, 17, 12, 19, 22, 9$

Solution: Write the numbers in order: $8, 9, 12, 13, 17, 19, 22$
The median is the number in the middle. Therefore, the median is 13.

Example 2. What is the mode of these numbers? $7, 6, 8, 6, 8, 7, 3, 7$

Solution: Mode: the value in the list that appears most often.
Therefore, the mode is number 7. There are three number 5 in the data.

Example 3. What is the mean of these numbers? $8, 3, 4, 3, 5, 9, 8, 6$

Solution: Mean: $\dfrac{sum\ of\ the\ data}{total\ number\ of\ data\ entires} = \dfrac{8+3+\ 4+3+5+\ 9+8+6}{8} = \dfrac{46}{8} = 5.75$

Example 4. What is the range in this list? $5, 9, 14, 8, 17, 22, 10$

Solution: Range is the difference of the largest value and smallest value in the list. The largest value is 22 and the smallest value is 5.
Then: $22 - 5 = 17$

bit.ly/2KO86gg

Find more at

Pie Graph

☆ A Pie Graph (Pie Chart) is a circle chart divided into sectors, each sector represents the relative size of each value.

☆ Pie charts represent a snapshot of how a group is broken down into smaller pieces.

Example:

A library has 820 books that include Mathematics, Physics, Chemistry, English and History. Use the following graph to answer the questions.

Example 1. What is the number of Mathematics books?

Solution: Number of total books = 820

Percent of Mathematics books = 30%

Then, the number of Mathematics books: $30\% \times 820 = 0.30 \times 820 = 246$

Example 2. What is the number of History books?

Solution: Number of total books = 820

Percent of History books = 10%

Then: $0.10 \times 820 = 82$

Example 3. What is the number of Chemistry books in the library?

Solution: Number of total books = 820

Percent of Chemistry books = 20%

Then: $0.20 \times 820 = 164$

Probability Problems

☆ Probability is the likelihood of something happening in the future. It is expressed as a number between zero (can never happen) to 1 (will always happen).

☆ Probability can be expressed as a fraction, a decimal, or a percent.

☆ Probability formula: $Probability = \frac{number\ of\ desired\ outcomes}{number\ of\ total\ outcomes}$

Examples:

Example 1. Anita's trick–or–treat bag contains 12 pieces of chocolate, 18 suckers, 18 pieces of gum, 24 pieces of licorice. If she randomly pulls a piece of candy from her bag, what is the probability of her pulling out a piece of sucker?

Solution: Probability $= \frac{number\ of\ desired\ outcomes}{number\ of\ total\ outcomes}$

Probability of pulling out a piece of sucker $= \frac{18}{12 + 18 + 18 + 24} = \frac{18}{72} = \frac{1}{4}$

Example 2. A bag contains 20 balls: four green, five black, eight blue, a brown, a red and one white. If 19 balls are removed from the bag at random, what is the probability that a brown ball has been removed?

Solution: If 19 balls are removed from the bag at random, there will be one ball in the bag. The probability of choosing a brown ball is 1 out of 20. Therefore, the probability of not choosing a brown ball is 19 out of 20 and the probability of having not a brown ball after removing 19 balls is the same. The answer is: $\frac{19}{20}$

Permutations and Combinations

☆ **Factorials** are products, indicated by an exclamation mark. For example, $4! = 4 \times 3 \times 2 \times 1$ (Remember that $0!$ is defined to be equal to 1)

☆ **Permutations:** The number of ways to choose a sample of k elements from a set of n distinct objects where order does matter, and replacements are not allowed. For a permutation problem, use this formula:

$$_nP_k = \frac{n!}{(n-k)!}$$

☆ **Combination:** The number of ways to choose a sample of r elements from a set of n distinct objects where order does not matter, and replacements are not allowed. For a combination problem, use this formula:

$$_nC_r = \frac{n!}{r!\,(n-r)!}$$

Examples:

Example 1. How many ways can the first and second place be awarded to 9 people?

Solution: Since the order matters, (the first and second place are different!) we need to use permutation formula where n is 9 and k is 2. Then: $\frac{n!}{(n-k)!} = \frac{9!}{(9-2)!} = \frac{9!}{7!} = \frac{9 \times 8 \times 7!}{7!}$, remove 7! from both sides of the fraction. Then: $\frac{9 \times 8 \times 7!}{7!} = 9 \times 8 = 72$

Example 2. How many ways can we pick a team of 4 people from a group of 7?

Solution: Since the order doesn't matter, we need to use a combination formula where n is 7 and r is 4.

Then: $\frac{n!}{r!\,(n-r)!} = \frac{7!}{4!\,(7-4)!} = \frac{7!}{4!\,(3)!} = \frac{7 \times 6 \times 5 \times 4!}{4!\,(3)!} = \frac{7 \times 6 \times 5}{3 \times 2 \times 1} = \frac{210}{6} = 35$

Day 19: Practices

✍ Find the values of the Given Data.

1) 8, 4, 10, 7, 3, 4

   Mode: _____   Range: _____

   Mean: _____   Median: _____

2) 16, 15, 15, 16, 13, 14, 23

   Mode: _____   Range: _____

   Mean: _____   Median: _____

✍ The circle graph below shows all Wilson's expenses for last month. Wilson spent $200 on his bills last month.

3) How much did Wilson spend on his clothes last month?
   _____

4) How much did Wilson spend for foods last month?
   _____

5) How much did Wilson spend on his books last month?
   _____

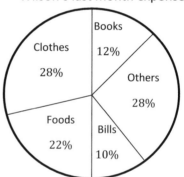

Wilson's last month expenses

Books 12%
Clothes 28%
Others 28%
Foods 22%
Bills 10%

✍ Solve.

6) There are 6 blue marbles, 8 red marbles, and 5 yellow marbles in a box. If Ava randomly selects a marble from the box, what is the probability of selecting a red or yellow marble? _____

✍ Solve.

7) A professor is going to arrange her 7 students in a straight line. In how many ways can she do this? _____

Effortless Math Education

Day 19: Answers

1) Mode: 4, Range: 7, Mean: 6, Median: 5.5

2) Mode: 15 and 16, Range: 10, Mean: 16, Median: 15

3) $560

6) $\frac{13}{19}$

4) $440

7) 5,040

5) $240

DAY 20 Functions

 Math topics that you'll learn in this chapter:

1. Function Notation and Evaluation
2. Adding and Subtracting Functions
3. Multiplying and Dividing Functions
4. Compositions of Functions

135

Function Notation and Evaluation

☆ Functions are mathematical operations that assign unique outputs to given inputs.

☆ Function notation is the way a function is written. It is meant to be a precise way of giving information about the function without a rather lengthy written explanation.

☆ The most popular function notation is $f(x)$ which is read "f of x". Any letter can name a function. for example: $g(x)$, $h(x)$, etc.

☆ To evaluate a function, plug in the input (the given value or expression) for the function's variable (place holder, x).

Examples:

Example 1. Evaluate: $f(x) = x + 8$, find $f(-2)$

Solution: Substitute x with -2:
Then: $f(x) = x + 8 \rightarrow f(-2) = -2 + 8 \rightarrow f(-2) = 6$

Example 2. Evaluate: $w(x) = 5x - 1$, find $w(3)$.

Solution: Substitute x with 3:
Then: $w(x) = 5x - 1 \rightarrow w(3) = 5(3) - 1 = 15 - 1 = 14$

Example 3. Evaluate: $f(x) = 3x^2 + 5$, find $f(-1)$.

Solution: Substitute x with -1:
Then: $f(x) = 3x^2 + 5 \rightarrow f(-1) = 3(-1)^2 + 5 \rightarrow f(-1) = 3 + 5 = 8$

Example 4. Evaluate: $h(x) = 2x^2 - 8$, find $h(2a)$.

Solution: Substitute x with $2a$:
Then: $\quad h(x) = 2x^2 - 8 \rightarrow h(2a) = 2(2a)^2 - 8 \rightarrow h(2a) = 2(4a^2) - 8 = 8a^2 - 8$

bit.ly/3mls7lF

Find more at

Adding and Subtracting Functions

★ Just like we can add and subtract numbers and expressions, we can add or subtract functions and simplify or evaluate them. The result is a new function.

★ For two functions $f(x)$ and $g(x)$, we can create two new functions:

$$(f + g)(x) = f(x) + g(x) \text{ and } (f - g)(x) = f(x) - g(x)$$

Examples:

Example 1. $g(x) = x - 3$, $f(x) = x + 1$, Find: $(g + f)(x)$

Solution: $(g + f)(x) = g(x) + f(x)$
Then: $(g + f)(x) = (x - 3) + (x + 1) = x - 3 + x + 1 = 2x - 2$

Example 2. $f(x) = 2x - 5$, $g(x) = x - 8$, Find: $(f - g)(x)$

Solution: $(f - g)(x) = f(x) - g(x)$
Then: $(f - g)(x) = (2x - 5) - (x - 8) = 2x - 5 - x + 8 = x + 3$

Example 3. $g(x) = x^2 + 6$, $f(x) = x + 7$, Find: $(g + f)(x)$

Solution: $(g + f)(x) = g(x) + f(x)$
Then: $(g + f)(x) = (x^2 + 6) + (x + 7) = x^2 + 6 + x + 7 = x^2 + x + 13$

Example 4. $f(x) = 3x^2 - 6$, $g(x) = 4x + 5$, Find: $(f - g)(3)$

Solution: $(f - g)(x) = f(x) - g(x)$
Then: $(f - g)(x) = (3x^2 - 6) - (4x + 5) = 3x^2 - 6 - 4x - 5 = 3x^2 - 4x - 11$
Substitute x with 3: $(f - g)(3) = 3(3)^2 - 4(3) - 11 =$
$27 - 12 - 11 = 4$

Multiplying and Dividing Functions

☆ Just like we can multiply and divide numbers and expressions, we can multiply and divide two functions and simplify or evaluate them.

☆ For two functions $f(x)$ and $g(x)$, we can create two new functions:

$$(f.g)(x) = f(x).g(x) \text{ and } \left(\frac{f}{g}\right)(x) = \frac{f(x)}{g(x)}$$

Examples:

Example 1. $g(x) = x + 4$, $f(x) = x + 5$, Find: $(g.f)(x)$

Solution:

$(g.f)(x) = g(x).f(x) = (x + 4)(x + 5) = x^2 + 5x + 4x + 20 = x^2 + 9x + 20$

Example 2. $f(x) = x + 8$, $h(x) = x - 7$, Find: $\left(\frac{f}{h}\right)(x)$

Solution: $\left(\frac{f}{h}\right)(x) = \frac{f(x)}{h(x)} = \frac{x+8}{x-7}$

Example 3. $g(x) = x + 9$, $f(x) = x - 5$, Find: $(g.f)(2)$

Solution: $(g.f)(x) = g(x).f(x) = (x + 9)(x - 5) = x^2 - 5x + 9x - 45$
$g(x).f(x) = x^2 + 4x - 45$
Substitute x with 2: $(g.f)(x) = (2)^2 + 4(2) - 45 = 4 + 8 - 45 = -33$

Example 4. $f(x) = x + 4$, $h(x) = 2x - 5$, Find: $\left(\frac{f}{h}\right)(3)$

Solution: $\left(\frac{f}{h}\right)(x) = \frac{f(x)}{h(x)}$
Substitute x with 3: $\left(\frac{f}{h}\right)(x) = \frac{x+4}{2x-5} = \frac{3+4}{2(3)-5} = \frac{7}{1} = 7$

bit.ly/3ph7kHA
Find more at

Composition of Functions

☆ "Composition of functions" simply means combining two or more functions in a way where the output from one function becomes the input for the next function.

☆ The notation used for composition is: $(fog)(x) = f(g(x))$ and is read

"f composed with g of x" or "f of g of x".

Examples:

Example 1. Using $f(x) = x - 5$ and $g(x) = 2x$, find: $(fog)(x)$

Solution: $(fog)(x) = f(g(x))$. Then: $(fog)(x) = f(g(x)) = f(2x)$

Now, find $f(2x)$ by substituting x with $2x$ in $f(x)$ function. Then: $f(x) = x - 5$

$$(x \to 2x) \to f(2x) = (2x) - 5 = 2x - 5$$

Example 2. Using $f(x) = 3x - 2$ and $g(x) = 2x - 5$, find: $(gof)(4)$

Solution: $(fog)(x) = f(g(x))$. Then: $(gof)(x) = g(f(x)) = g(3x - 2)$,

Now substitute x in $g(x)$ by $(3x - 2)$.

Then: $g(3x - 2) = 2(3x - 2) - 5 = 6x - 4 - 5 = 6x - 9$

Substitute x with 4: $(gof)(4) = g(f(x)) = 6x - 9 = 6(4) - 9 = 24 - 9 = 15$

Example 3. Using $f(x) = x^2 - 6$ and $g(x) = x + 3$, find: $f(g(3))$

Solution: First, find $g(3)$: $g(x) = x + 3 \to g(3) = 3 + 3 = 6$

Then: $f(g(3)) = f(6)$. Now, find $f(6)$ by substituting x with 6 in $f(x)$ function.

$f(g(3)) = f(6) = (6)^2 - 6 = 36 - 6 = 30$

Day 20: Practices

✎ **Evaluate each function.**

1) $g(n) = 3n + 5$, find $g(2)$

2) $h(x) = 4n - 8$, find $h(4)$

3) $k(n) = 12 - 3n$, find $k(2)$

4) $g(x) = -5x + 6$, find $g(-2)$

✎ **Perform the indicated operation.**

5) $h(t) = 5t + 6$
$g(t) = 2t + 4$
$Find\,(h + g)(x)$

_____

6) $g(a) = -6a + 1$
$f(a) = 3a^2 - 3$
$Find\,(g + f)(5)$

_____

✎ **Perform the indicated operation.**

7) $g(a) = a - 8$
$h(a) = 4a - 2$
$Find\,(g.h)(3)$

_____

8) $f(x) = 6x + 2$
$h(x) = 5x - 1$
$Find\left(\frac{f}{h}\right)(-2)$

_____

✎ **Using $f(x) = 4x + 3$ and $g(x) = x - 7$, find:**

9) $g\big(f(2)\big) =$ _____

10) $g\big(f(-2)\big) =$ _____

11) $f\big(g(4)\big) =$ _____

12) $f\big(f(7)\big) =$ _____

Effortless Math Education

Day 20: Answers

1) 11

2) 8

3) 6

4) 16

5) $7t + 10$

6) 43

7) -50

8) $\frac{10}{11}$

9) 4

10) -12

11) -9

12) 127

Effortless Math Education

DAY 21 Quadratic

 Math topics that you'll learn in this chapter:

1. Solving a Quadratic Equation
2. Graphing Quadratic Functions
3. Solving Quadratic Inequalities
4. Graphing Quadratic Inequalities

143

Solving a Quadratic Equation

☆ Write the equation in the form of: $ax^2 + bx + c = 0$

☆ Factorize the quadratic, set each factor equal to zero and solve.

☆ Use quadratic formula if you couldn't factorize the quadratic.

☆ Quadratic formula: $x = \frac{-b \pm \sqrt{b^2 - 4ac}}{2a}$

Examples:

Find the solutions of each quadratic function.

Example 1. $x^2 + 5x + 6 = 0$

Solution: Factor the quadratic by grouping. We need to find two numbers whose sum is 5 (from $5x$) and whose product is 6. Those numbers are 2 and 3. Then: $x^2 + 5x + 6 = 0 \rightarrow x^2 + 2x + 3x + 6 = 0 \rightarrow (x^2 + 2x) + (3x + 6) = 0$, Now, find common factors: $(x^2 + 2x) = x(x + 2)$ and $(3x + 6) = 3(x + 2)$. We have two expressions $(x^2 + 2x)$ and $(3x + 6)$ and their common factor is $(x + 2)$. Then: $(x^2 + 2x) + (3x + 6) = 0 \rightarrow x(x + 2) + 3(x + 2) = 0 \rightarrow (x + 2)(x + 3) = 0$.
The product of two expressions is 0. Then:
$(x + 2) = 0 \rightarrow x = -2$ or $(x + 3) = 0 \rightarrow x = -3$

Example 2. $x^2 + 8x + 15 = 0$

Solution: Use quadratic formula: $x_{1,2} = \frac{-b \pm \sqrt{b^2 - 4ac}}{2a}$, $a = 1, b = 8$ and $c = 15$

Then:

$$x = \frac{-8 \pm \sqrt{8^2 - 4 \times 1(15)}}{2(1)}, x_1 = \frac{-8 + \sqrt{8^2 - 4 \times 1(15)}}{2(1)} = -3, x_2 = \frac{-8 - \sqrt{8^2 - 4 \times 1(15)}}{2(1)} = -5$$

bit.ly/3ehZhYk

Graphing Quadratic Functions

☆ Quadratic functions in vertex form: $y = a(x - h)^2 + k$ where (h, k) is the vertex of the function. The axis of symmetry is $x = h$

☆ Quadratic functions in standard form: $y = ax^2 + bx + c$ where $x = -\frac{b}{2a}$ is the value of x in the vertex of the function.

☆ To graph a quadratic function, first find the vertex, then substitute some values for x and solve for y. (Remember that the graph of a quadratic function is a U-shaped curve and it is called "parabola".)

Example:

Example 1. Sketch the graph of $y = (x + 3)^2 - 4$

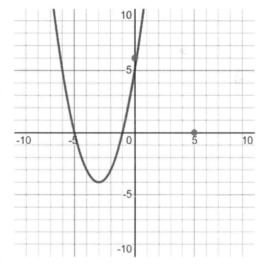

Solution: Quadratic functions in vertex form:
$y = a(x - h)^2 + k$ and (h, k) is the vertex. Then, the vertex of $y = (x + 3)^2 - 4$ is $(-3, -4)$.

Substitute zero for x and solve for y:
$y = (0 + 3)^2 - 4 = 5$.
The y Intercept is $(0, 5)$.

Now, you can simply graph the quadratic function. Notice that quadratic function is a U-shaped curve.

Solving Quadratic Inequalities

☆ A quadratic inequality is one that can be written in the standard form of

$ax^2 + bx + c > 0$ (or substitute $<, \leq,$ or $\geq$ for $>$).

☆ Solving a quadratic inequality is like solving equations. We need to find the solutions (the zeroes).

☆ To solve quadratic inequalities, first find quadratic equations. Then choose a test value between zeroes. Finally, find interval(s), such as > 0 or < 0.

Examples:

Example 1. Solve quadratic inequality. $x^2 + 2x - 15 > 0$

Solution: First solve $x^2 + 2x - 15 = 0$ by factoring. Then: $x^2 + 2x - 15 = 0 \rightarrow$ $(x - 3)(x + 5) = 0$. The product of two expressions is 0. Then: $(x - 3) = 0 \rightarrow$ $x = 3$ or $(x + 5) = 0 \rightarrow x = -5$. Now, choose a value between 3 and -5. Let's choose 0. Then: $x = 0 \rightarrow x^2 + 2x - 15 > 0 \rightarrow (0)^2 + 2(0) - 15 > 0 \rightarrow -15 > 0$ -15 is not greater than 0. Therefore, all values between 3 and -5 are NOT the solution of this quadratic inequality. The solution is: $x > 3$ and $x < -5$. To represent the solution, we can use interval notation, in which solution sets are indicated with parentheses or brackets. The solutions $x > 3$ and $x < -5$ represented as: $(-\infty, -5) \cup (3, \infty)$

Example 2. Solve quadratic inequality. $x^2 + 9x + 18 \geq 0$

Solution: First solve: $x^2 + 9x + 18$, Factor: $x^2 + 9x + 18 \rightarrow$ $(x + 3)(x + 6) = 0$.
-3 and -6 are the solutions. Choose a point between -3 and -6. Let's choose -4. Then: $x = -4 \rightarrow x^2 + 9x + 18 \geq 0 \rightarrow (-4)^2 + 9(-4) + 18 \geq 0 \rightarrow -2 \geq 0$.

This is NOT true. So, the solution is: $x \leq -6$ or $x \geq -3$

(using interval notation the solution is: $(\infty, -6] \cup [-3, \infty)$

bit.ly/3uk7ukw

Find more at

Graphing Quadratic Inequalities

✰ A quadratic inequality is in the form

$$y > ax^2 + bx + c \text{ (or substitute } <, \leq, \text{ or } \geq \text{ for } >).$$

✰ To graph a quadratic inequality, start by graphing the quadratic parabola. Then fill in the region either inside or outside of it, depending on the inequality.

✰ Choose a testing point and check the solution section.

Example:

Example 1. Sketch the graph of $y > 3x^2$

Solution: First, graph the quadratic $y = 3x^2$
Since the inequality sing is $>$, we need to use dash lines.

Now, choose a testing point inside the parabola. Let's choose $(0, 3)$.

$$y > 3x^2 \rightarrow 3 > 3(0)^2 \rightarrow 3 > 0$$

This is true. So, inside the parabola is the solution section.

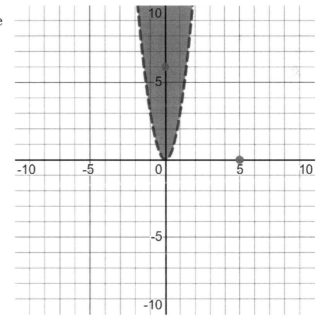

Day 21: Practices

✍ **Solve each equation by factoring or using the quadratic formula.**

1) $x^2 + 5x - 14 = 0$

2) $x^2 + 3x - 40 = 0$

_____

_____

✍ **Sketch the graph of each function.**

3) $y = (x + 2)^2 - 4$

4) $y = (x - 3)^2 + 5$

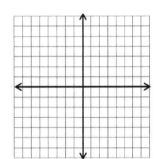

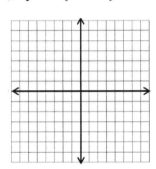

✍ **Solve each quadratic inequality.**

5) $x^2 - 10x + 24 > 0$

6) $x^2 - 4x - 21 \geq 0$

_____

_____

✍ **Sketch the graph of each quadratic inequality.**

7) $y < -3x^2$

8) $y > 4x^2$

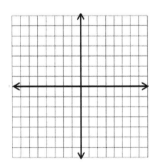

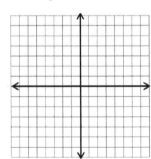

Effortless Math Education

Day 21: Answers

1) $x = -7, x = 2$

2) $x = -8, x = 5$

3)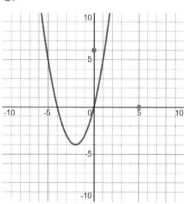

4)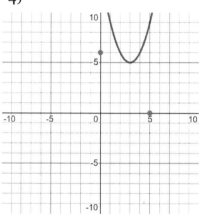

5) $4 \le x \le 6$

6) $x \le -3 \ or \ x \ge 7$

7)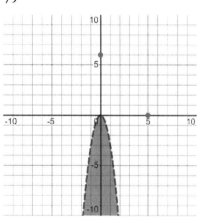

8)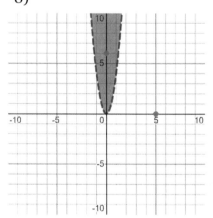

**Effortless
Math
Education**

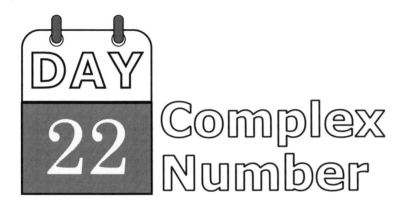
DAY 22 Complex Number

Math topics that you'll learn in this chapter:

1. Adding and Subtracting Complex Numbers

2. Multiplying and Dividing Complex Numbers

3. Rationalizing Imaginary Denominators

151

Adding and Subtracting Complex Numbers

✩ A complex number is expressed in the form $a + bi$, where a and b are real numbers, and i, which is called an imaginary number, is a solution of the equation $x^2 = -1$

✩ For adding complex numbers:

$$(a + bi) + (c + di) = (a + c) + (b + d)i$$

✩ For subtracting complex numbers:

$$(a + bi) - (c + di) = (a - c) + (b - d)i$$

Examples:

Example 1. Solve: $(5 + 4i) + (9 - 3i)$

Solution: Remove parentheses: $(5 + 4i) + (9 - 2i) = 5 + 4i + 9 - 3i$
Combine like terms: $5 + 4i + 9 - 3i = 14 + i$

Example 2. Solve: $(12 + 6i) + (4 - 3i)$

Solution: Remove parentheses: $(12 + 6i) + (4 - 3i) = 12 + 6i + 4 - 3i$
Group like terms: $12 + 6i + 4 - 3i = 16 + 3i$

Example 3. Solve: $(-7 - 4i) - (3 + 5i)$

Solution: Remove parentheses by multiplying -1 to the second parentheses:
$(-7 - 4i) - (3 + 5i) = -7 - 4i - 3 - 5i$

Combine like terms: $-7 - 4i - 3 - 5i = -10 - 9i$

Multiplying and Dividing Complex Numbers

☆ You can use FOIL (First-Out-In-Last) method or the following rule to multiply imaginary numbers. Remember that: $i^2 = -1$

$$(a + bi) + (c + di) = (ac - bd) + (ad + bc)i$$

☆ To divide complex numbers, you need to find the conjugate of the denominator. Conjugate of $(a + bi)$ is $(a - bi)$.

☆ Dividing complex numbers: $\frac{a+bi}{c+di} = \frac{a+bi}{c+di} \times \frac{c-di}{c-di} = \frac{ac+bd}{c^2+d^2} + \frac{bc-ad}{c^2+d^2}i$

Examples:

Example 1. Solve: $\frac{5-2i}{3+i}$

Solution: Use the rule for dividing complex numbers: $\frac{a+bi}{c+di} = \frac{a+bi}{c+di} \times \frac{c-di}{c-di} =$

$\frac{ac+bd}{c^2+d^2} + \frac{bc-ad}{c^2+d^2}i \rightarrow \frac{5-2i}{3+i} \times \frac{3-i}{3-i} = \frac{(5\times3+(-2)\times1)+(-2\times3-5\times1)i}{3^2+1^2} = \frac{13-11i}{10} = \frac{13}{10} - \frac{11}{10}i$

Example 2. Solve: $(4 - 3i)(5 - 3i)$

Solution: Use the multiplication of imaginary numbers rule:
$(a + bi) + (c + di) = (ac - bd) + (ad + bc)i$
$\left(4 \times 5 - (-3)(-3)\right) + (4(-3) + (-3) \times 5)i = 11 - 27i$

Example 3. Solve: $\frac{8-2i}{2+i}$

Solution: The conjugate of $(2 + i)$ is $(2 - i)$. Use the rule for dividing complex numbers:

$$\frac{a+bi}{c+di} = \frac{a+bi}{c+di} \times \frac{c-di}{c-di} = \frac{ac+bd}{c^2+d^2} + \frac{bc-ad}{c^2+d^2}i \rightarrow$$

$\frac{8-2i}{2+i} \times \frac{2-i}{2-i} = \frac{8\times(2)+(-2)(1)}{2^2+(1)^2} + \frac{-2\times2-(8)(1)}{2^2+(1)^2}i = \frac{14}{5} + \frac{-12}{5}i = \frac{14}{5} - \frac{12}{5}i$

Rationalizing Imaginary Denominators

★ Step 1: Find the conjugate (it's the denominator with different sign between the two terms).

★ Step 2: Multiply numerator and denominator by the conjugate.

★ Step 3: Simplify if needed.

Examples:

Example 1. Solve: $\frac{4-3i}{6i}$

Solution: Multiply both numerator and denominator by $\frac{i}{i}$:

$$\frac{4-3i}{6i} = \frac{(4-3i)(i)}{6i(i)} = \frac{(4)(i)-(3i)(i)}{6(i^2)} = \frac{4i-3i^2}{6(-1)} = \frac{4i-3(-1)}{-6} = \frac{4i}{-6} + \frac{3}{-6} = -\frac{1}{2} - \frac{2}{3}i$$

Example 2. Solve: $\frac{6i}{2-i}$

Solution: Multiply both numerator and denominator by the conjugate

$$\frac{2+i}{2+i}: \frac{6i(2+i)}{(2-i)(2+i)} = \text{Apply complex arithmetic rule: } (a+bi)(a-bi) = a^2 + b^2$$

$$2^2 + (-1)^2 = 5, \text{ then: } \frac{6i(2+i)}{(2-i)(2+i)} = \frac{-6+12i}{5} = -\frac{6}{5} + \frac{12}{5}i$$

Example 3. Solve: $\frac{8-2i}{2i}$

Solution: Factor 2 from both sides: $\frac{8-2i}{2i} = \frac{2(4-i)}{2i}$, divide both sides by 2:

$$\frac{2(4-i)}{2i} = \frac{(4-i)}{i}$$

Multiply both numerator and denominator by $\frac{i}{i}$:

$$\frac{(4-i)}{i} = \frac{(4-i)}{i} \times \frac{i}{i} = \frac{(4i-i^2)}{i^2} = \frac{1+4i}{-1} = -1-4i$$

bit.ly/3vC5eoO

Find more at

Day 22: Practices

✎ Evaluate.

1) $(-3i) - (5i) =$

2) $(-4i) + (-6i) =$

3) $(5i) - (5 + 3i) =$

4) $(5 - 8i) + (-2i) =$

5) $(-5i) + (3 + 5i) =$

6) $12 + (-2 - 8i) =$

7) $(-4i) - (8 + 2i) =$

8) $(6 + 9i) - (-5i) =$

✎ Calculate.

9) $(2 - 3i)(4 - 3i) =$

10) $(8 + 2i)(4 + 2i) =$

11) $(8 - i)(4 - 2i) =$

12) $(2 - 4i)(3 - 5i) =$

13) $(4 + 4i)(3 + 2i) =$

14) $(5 + 3i)(9 + 2i) =$

15) $(6 - 3i)(8 - 2i) =$

16) $(9 - 3i)(8 - 4i) =$

✎ Simplify.

17) $\frac{2-3i}{-5i} =$

18) $\frac{4-5i}{-2i} =$

19) $\frac{8+3i}{2i} =$

20) $\frac{8-3i}{2+i} =$

21) $\frac{6-2i}{4+2i} =$

22) $\frac{8+3i}{6+i} =$

23) $\frac{7+2i}{3-2i} =$

24) $\frac{5-i}{6+i} =$

Day 22: Answers

1) $-8i$

2) $-10i$

3) $2i - 5$

4) $5 - 10i$

5) 3

6) $10 - 8i$

7) $-8 - 6i$

8) $6 + 14i$

9) $-1 - 18i$

10) $28 + 24i$

11) $30 - 20i$

12) $-14 - 22i$

13) $4 + 20i$

14) $39 + 37i$

15) $42 - 36i$

16) $60 - 60i$

17) $\frac{3}{5} + \frac{2}{5}i$

18) $\frac{5}{2} + 2i$

19) $\frac{3}{2} - 4i$

20) $\frac{13}{5} - \frac{14}{5}i$

21) $1 - i$

22) $\frac{51}{37} + \frac{10}{37}i$

23) $\frac{17}{13} + \frac{20}{13}i$

24) $\frac{29}{37} - \frac{11}{37}i$

**Effortless
Math
Education**

DAY 23 Radicals

Math topics that you'll learn in this chapter:

1. Simplifying Radical Expressions

2. Adding and Subtracting Radical Expressions

3. Multiplying Radical Expressions

157

Simplifying Radical Expressions

☆ Find the prime factors of the numbers or expressions inside the radical.

☆ Use radical properties to simplify the radical expression:

$$\sqrt[n]{x^a} = x^{\frac{a}{n}}, \quad \sqrt[n]{xy} = x^{\frac{1}{n}} \times y^{\frac{1}{n}}, \quad \sqrt[n]{\frac{x}{y}} = \frac{x^{\frac{1}{n}}}{y^{\frac{1}{n}}}, \text{ and } \sqrt[n]{x} \times \sqrt[n]{y} = \sqrt[n]{xy}$$

Examples:

Example 1. Simplify. $\sqrt{16x^3}$

Solution: First factor the expression $16x^3$: $16x^3 = 4^2 \times x \times x \times x$, we need to find perfect squares: $16x^3 = 4^2 \times x^2 \times x$,
Then: $\sqrt{16x^3} = \sqrt{4^2 \times x^2} \times \sqrt{x}$
Now use radical rule: $\sqrt[n]{a^n} = a$, Then: $\sqrt{4^2 \times x^2} \times \sqrt{x} = 4x \times \sqrt{x} = 4x\sqrt{x}$

Example 2. Find the square root of $\sqrt{121x^2}$.

Solution: Find the factor of the expression $121x^2$: $121 = 11 \times 11$ and $x^2 = x \times x$, now use radical rule: $\sqrt[n]{a^n} = a$, Then: $\sqrt{11^2} = 11$ and $\sqrt{x^2} = x$
Finally: $\sqrt{121x^2} = \sqrt{11^2} \times \sqrt{x^2} = 11 \times x = 11x$

Example 3. Write this radical in exponential form. $\sqrt[3]{x^5}$

Solution: To write a radical in exponential form, use this rule: $\sqrt[n]{x^a} = x^{\frac{a}{n}}$
Then: $\sqrt[3]{x^5} = x^{\frac{5}{3}}$

Example 4. Simplify. $\sqrt{8a^5b^4}$

Solution: First factor the expression $8a^5b^4$: $8a^5b^4 = 2^3 \times a^5 \times b^4$, we need to find perfect squares: $8a^5b^4 = 2^2 \times 2 \times a^4 \times a \times b^4$, Then:
$\sqrt{8a^5b^4} = \sqrt{2^2 \times a^4 \times b^4} \times \sqrt{2a}$
Now use radical rule: $\sqrt[n]{a^n} = a$, Then:
$\sqrt{2^2 \times a^4 \times b^4} \times \sqrt{2a} = 2 \times a^2 \times b^2 \times \sqrt{2a} = 2a^2b^2\sqrt{2a}$

Adding and Subtracting Radical Expressions

☆ Only numbers and expressions that have the same radical part can be added or subtracted.

☆ Remember, combining "unlike" radical terms is not possible.

☆ For numbers with the same radical part, just add or subtract factors outside the radicals.

Examples:

Example 1. Simplify: $7\sqrt{3} + 4\sqrt{3}$

Solution: Since we have the same radical parts, then we can add these two radicals: Add like terms: $7\sqrt{3} + 4\sqrt{3} = 11\sqrt{3}$

Example 2. Simplify: $12\sqrt{5} + 8\sqrt{5}$

Solution: Since we have the same radical parts, then we can add these two radicals: Add like terms: $12\sqrt{5} + 8\sqrt{5} = 20\sqrt{5}$

Example 3. Simplify: $5\sqrt{8} - 2\sqrt{2}$

Solution: The two radical parts are not the same. First, we need to simplify the $5\sqrt{8}$. Then: $5\sqrt{8} = 5\sqrt{4 \times 2} = 5(\sqrt{4})(\sqrt{2}) = 10\sqrt{2}$
Now, combine like terms: $5\sqrt{8} - 2\sqrt{2} = 10\sqrt{2} - 2\sqrt{2} = 8\sqrt{2}$

Example 4. Simplify: $8\sqrt{27} + 5\sqrt{3}$

Solution: The two radical parts are not the same. First, we need to simplify the $8\sqrt{27}$. Then: $8\sqrt{27} = 8\sqrt{9 \times 3} = 8(\sqrt{9})(\sqrt{3}) = 24\sqrt{3}$
Now, add: $8\sqrt{27} + 5\sqrt{3} = 24\sqrt{3} + 3\sqrt{3} = 27\sqrt{3}$

Multiplying Radical Expressions

To multiply radical expressions:

☆ Multiply the numbers and expressions outside of the radicals.

☆ Multiply the numbers and expressions inside the radicals.

☆ Simplify if needed.

Examples:

Example 1. Evaluate. $4\sqrt{7} \times 2\sqrt{3}$

Solution: Multiply the numbers outside of the radicals and the radical parts.
Then: $4\sqrt{7} \times 2\sqrt{3} = 4 \times 2 \times \sqrt{7} \times \sqrt{3} = 8\sqrt{21}$

Example 2. Multiply. $4x\sqrt{3} \times 6\sqrt{x}$

Solution: Multiply the numbers outside of the radicals and the radical parts.
Then, simplify: $4x\sqrt{3} \times 6\sqrt{x} = (4x \times 6) \times (\sqrt{3} \times \sqrt{x}) = (24x)(\sqrt{3x}) = 24x\sqrt{3x}$

Example 3. Evaluate. $6a\sqrt{7b} \times 3\sqrt{2b}$

Solution: Multiply the numbers outside of the radicals and the radical parts.
Then: $6a\sqrt{7b} \times 3\sqrt{2b} = 6a \times 3 \times \sqrt{7b} \times \sqrt{2b} = 18a\sqrt{14b^2}$
Simplify: $18a\sqrt{14b^2} = 18a \times \sqrt{14} \times \sqrt{b^2} = 18ab\sqrt{14}$

Example 4. Simplify. $9\sqrt{9x} \times 5\sqrt{4x}$

Solution: Multiply the numbers outside of the radicals and the radical parts.
Then, simplify: $9\sqrt{9x} \times 5\sqrt{4x} = (9 \times 5) \times (\sqrt{9x} \times \sqrt{4x}) = (45)(\sqrt{36x^2}) = 45\sqrt{36x^2}$

$\sqrt{36x^2} = 6x$, then: $45\sqrt{36x^2} = 45 \times 6x = 270x$

bit.ly/39dJc2Z

Find more at

Day 23: Practices

✎ Simplify.

1) $\sqrt{169} =$

2) $\sqrt{256y} =$

3) $\sqrt{900} =$

4) $\sqrt{49x^2} =$

5) $\sqrt{25b^4} =$

6) $\sqrt{121y^4} =$

7) $\sqrt{144a^2b} =$

8) $\sqrt{36 \times 9} =$

✎ Simplify.

9) $3\sqrt{5} + 2\sqrt{5} =$

10) $4\sqrt{3} - 2\sqrt{3} =$

11) $6\sqrt{6} + \sqrt{24} =$

12) $6\sqrt{3} + 4\sqrt{27} =$

13) $5\sqrt{2} + 10\sqrt{18} =$

14) $3\sqrt{7} - \sqrt{28} =$

15) $7\sqrt{2} - 5\sqrt{8} =$

16) $\sqrt{7} + 7\sqrt{63} =$

✎ Evaluate.

17) $\sqrt{5} \times \sqrt{3} =$

18) $\sqrt{6} \times \sqrt{8} =$

19) $3\sqrt{5} \times \sqrt{9} =$

20) $2\sqrt{3} \times 3\sqrt{7} =$

21) $\sqrt{6x} \times 5\sqrt{6x} =$

22) $\sqrt{4x} \times 2\sqrt{6x} =$

23) $\sqrt{2x^5} \times 2\sqrt{8x} =$

24) $-9\sqrt{3b^2} \times (-\sqrt{6}) =$

Effortless Math Education

Day 23: Answers

1) 13

2) $16\sqrt{y}$

3) 30

4) $7x$

5) $5b^2$

6) $11y^2$

7) $12a\sqrt{b}$

8) 18

9) $5\sqrt{5}$

10) $2\sqrt{3}$

11) $8\sqrt{6}$

12) $18\sqrt{3}$

13) $35\sqrt{2}$

14) $\sqrt{7}$

15) $-3\sqrt{2}$

16) $24\sqrt{7}$

17) $\sqrt{15}$

18) $\sqrt{48} = 4\sqrt{3}$

19) $9\sqrt{5}$

20) $6\sqrt{21}$

21) $30\sqrt{x}$

22) $4x\sqrt{6}$

23) $8x^3$

24) $27b\sqrt{2}$

Effortless Math Education

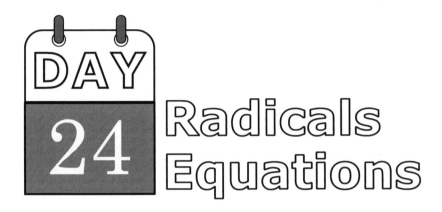

DAY 24 Radicals Equations

Math topics that you'll learn in this chapter:

1. Rationalizing Radical Expressions

2. Radical Equations

3. Domain and Range of Radical Functions

163

Rationalizing Radical Expressions

☆ Radical expressions cannot be in the denominator. (number in the bottom)

☆ To get rid of the radical in the denominator, multiply both numerator and denominator by the radical in the denominator.

☆ If there is a radical and another integer in the denominator, multiply both numerator and denominator by the conjugate of the denominator.

☆ The conjugate of $(a + b)$ is $(a - b)$ and vice versa.

Examples:

Example 1. Simplify: $\frac{9}{\sqrt{3}}$

Solution: Multiply both numerator and denominator by $\sqrt{3}$. Then:

$\frac{9}{\sqrt{3}} \times \frac{\sqrt{3}}{\sqrt{3}} = \frac{9\sqrt{3}}{\sqrt{9}} = \frac{9\sqrt{3}}{3}$, Now, simplify: $\frac{9\sqrt{3}}{3} = 3\sqrt{3}$

Example 2. Simplify: $\frac{5}{\sqrt{6} - 4}$

Solution: Multiply by the conjugate: $\frac{\sqrt{6} + 4}{\sqrt{6} + 4} \rightarrow \frac{5}{\sqrt{6} - 4} \times \frac{\sqrt{6} + 4}{\sqrt{6} + 4}$

$(\sqrt{6} - 4)(\sqrt{6} + 4) = -10$, then: $\frac{5}{\sqrt{6} - 4} \times \frac{\sqrt{6} + 4}{\sqrt{6} + 4} = \frac{5(\sqrt{6} + 4)}{-10}$

Use the fraction rule: $\frac{a}{-b} = -\frac{a}{b} \rightarrow \frac{5(\sqrt{6} + 4)}{-10} = -\frac{5(\sqrt{6} + 4)}{10} = -\frac{1}{2}(\sqrt{6} + 4)$

Example 3. Simplify: $\frac{6}{\sqrt{2} - 1}$

Solution: Multiply by the conjugate: $\frac{\sqrt{2} + 1}{\sqrt{2} + 1}$

$\frac{6}{\sqrt{2} - 1} \times \frac{\sqrt{2} + 1}{\sqrt{2} + 1} = \frac{6(\sqrt{2} + 1)}{1} = 6(\sqrt{2} + 1)$

bit.ly/3vKudGO
Find more at

Radical Equations

To solve a radical equation:

☆ Isolate the radical on one side of the equation.

☆ Square both sides of the equation to remove the radical.

☆ Solve the equation for the variable.

☆ Plugin the answer (answers) into the original equation to avoid extraneous values.

Examples:

Example 1. Solve $\sqrt{x} + 6 = 16$

Solution: Subtract 6 from both sides: $\sqrt{x} = 10$

Square both sides:

$\left(\sqrt{x}\right)^2 = 10^2 \rightarrow x = 100$

Plug in the value of 100 for x in the original equation and check the answer:

$x = 100 \rightarrow \sqrt{x} - 6 = \sqrt{100} - 6 = 10 - 6 = 4$

So, the value of 100 for x is correct.

Example 2. What is the value of x in this equation?

$$4\sqrt{x + 2} = 8$$

Solution: Divide both sides by 4. Then:

$4\sqrt{x + 2} = 8 \rightarrow \frac{4\sqrt{x+2}}{4} = \frac{8}{4} \rightarrow \sqrt{x + 2} = 2$

Square both sides: $\left(\sqrt{(x + 2)}\right)^2 = 2^2$, Then: $x + 2 = 4 \rightarrow x = 2$

Substitute x by 2 in the original equation and check the answer:

$x = 2 \rightarrow 4\sqrt{x + 2} = 4\sqrt{2 + 2} = 4\sqrt{4} = 4(2) = 8$

So, the value of 2 for x is correct.

Domain and Range of Radical Functions

☆ To find the domain of a radical function, find all possible values of the variable inside radical.

☆ Remember that having a negative number under the square root symbol is not possible. (For cubic roots, we can have negative numbers)

☆ To find the range, plug in the minimum and maximum values of the variable inside radical.

Example:

Example 1. Find the domain and range of the radical function. $y = \sqrt{x - 5}$

Solution: For domain: Find non-negative values for radicals: $x - 5 \geq 0$

Domain of functions: $x - 5 \geq 0 \rightarrow x \geq 5$

Domain of the function $y = \sqrt{x - 5}$: $x \geq 5$

For range: The range of a radical function of the form $c\sqrt{ax + b} + k$ is: $f(x) \geq k$

For the function $y = \sqrt{x - 5}$, the value of k is 0. Then: $f(x) \geq 0$

Range of the function $y = \sqrt{x - 5}$: $f(x) \geq 0$

Example 2. Find the domain and range of the radical function. $y = 6\sqrt{4x + 8} + 5$

Solution: For domain: Find non-negative values for radicals: $4x + 8 \geq 0$

Domain of functions: $4x + 8 \geq 0 \rightarrow 4x \geq -8 \rightarrow x \geq -2$

Domain of the function $y = 6\sqrt{4x + 8} + 5$: $x \geq -2$

For range: The range of a radical function of the form $c\sqrt{ax + b} + k$ is: $f(x) \geq k$

For the function $y = 6\sqrt{4x + 8} + 5$, the value of k is 5. Then: $f(x) \geq 5$

Range of the function $y = 6\sqrt{4x + 8} + 5$: $f(x) \geq 5$

bit.ly/2Pn4vlj

Find more at

Day 24: Practices

✎ Simplify.

1) $\dfrac{5}{\sqrt{6}} =$

2) $\dfrac{1}{\sqrt{2}-4} =$

3) $\dfrac{3}{\sqrt{2}+5} =$

4) $\dfrac{1}{\sqrt{3}-6} =$

5) $\dfrac{5}{\sqrt{2}+7} =$

6) $\dfrac{\sqrt{3}}{1-\sqrt{6}} =$

7) $\dfrac{2}{\sqrt{3}+5} =$

8) $\dfrac{\sqrt{2}}{1-\sqrt{8}} =$

✎ Solve for x.

9) $\sqrt{x} - 4 = 6$

10) $8 - \sqrt{x} = 4$

11) $\sqrt{x} + 2 = 9$

12) $3 + \sqrt{x} = 12$

13) $\sqrt{x} + 5 = 30$

14) $\sqrt{x} - 9 = 27$

15) $10 = \sqrt{x+1}$

16) $\sqrt{x+4} = 3$

✎ Identify the domain and range of each function.

17) $y = \sqrt{x+2}$

18) $y = \sqrt{x-6}$

19) $y = \sqrt{x+2} - 1$

20) $y = \sqrt{x+1}$

21) $y = \sqrt{x-4}$

22) $y = \sqrt{x-3} + 1$

23) $y = \sqrt{2x+8}$

24) $y = 6\sqrt{4x+8} + 8$

Effortless Math Education

Day 24: Answers

1) $\dfrac{5\sqrt{6}}{6}$

2) $-\dfrac{\sqrt{2}+4}{14}$

3) $-\dfrac{3(\sqrt{2}-5)}{23}$

4) $-\dfrac{\sqrt{3}+6}{33}$

5) $-\dfrac{5(\sqrt{2}-7)}{47}$

6) $-\dfrac{\sqrt{3}+3\sqrt{2}}{5}$

7) $-\dfrac{\sqrt{3}-5}{11}$

8) $-\dfrac{\sqrt{2}+4}{7}$

9) $x = 100$

10) $x = 16$

11) $x = 49$

12) $x = 81$

13) $x = 625$

14) $x = 1,296$

15) $x = 99$

16) $x = 5$

17) $x \geq -2, y \geq 0$

18) $x \geq 6, y \geq 0$

19) $x \geq -2, y \geq -1$

20) $x \geq -1, y \geq 0$

21) $x \geq 4, y \geq 0$

22) $x \geq 3, y \geq 1$

23) $x \geq -4, y \geq 0$

24) $x \geq -2, y \geq 0$

DAY 25 Logarithms

Math topics that you'll learn in this chapter:

1. Evaluating Logarithms
2. Expanding and Condensing Logarithms
3. Natural Logarithm
4. Solving Logarithmic Equations

169

Evaluating Logarithms

☆ Logarithm is another way of writing exponent. $log_b{}^y = x$ is equivalent to $y = b^x$.

☆ Learn some logarithms rules: ($a > 0, a \neq 0, M > 0, N > 0$, and k is a real number.)

Rule 1: $log_a(M.N) = log_a M + log_a N$

Rule 4: $log_a a = 1$

Rule 2: $log_a \frac{M}{N} = log_a M - log_a N$

Rule 5: $log_a{}^1 = 0$

Rule 3: $log_a(M)^k = k log_a M$

Rule 6: $a^{log_a k} = k$

Examples:

Example 1. Evaluate: $log_2 16$

Solution: Rewrite 16 in power base form: $16 = 2^4$, then: $log_2 16 = log_2(2^4)$

Use *log* rule: $log_a(M)^k = k.log_a(M) \rightarrow log_2(2^4) = 4log_2(2)$

Use *log* rule: $log_a(a) = 1 \rightarrow log_2(2) = 1.$ $4log_2(2) = 4 \times 1 = 4$

Example 2. Evaluate: $3log_4 256$

Solution: Rewrite 256 in power base form: $256 = 4^4$, then: $log_4 256 = log_4(4^4)$

Use *log* rule: $log_a(M)^k = k.log_a(M) \rightarrow log_4(256^4) = 4log_4(4)$

Use *log* rule: $log_a(a) = 1 \rightarrow log_4(4) = 1.$ $3 \times 4log_4(4) = 3 \times 4 = 12$

Example 3. Evaluate: $log_5(5)^5$

Solution: Use *log* rule: $log_a(M)^k = k.log_a(M) \rightarrow log_5(5)^5 = 5log_5(5)$

Use *log* rule: $log_a(a) = 1 \rightarrow log_5(5) = 1 \rightarrow 5 \times log_5(5) = 5 \times 1 = 5$

bit.ly/3hpkvDG

Find more at

Expanding and Condensing Logarithms

✰ Using some of properties of logs, (the product rule, quotient rule, and power rule) sometimes we can expand a logarithm expression (expanding) or convert some logarithm expressions into a single logarithm (condensing).

✰ Let's review some logarithms properties:

$$a^{log_a b} = b \qquad\qquad log_a \frac{1}{x} = -log_a x$$

$$log_a 1 = 0 \qquad\qquad log_a x^p = p\, log_a x$$

$$log_a a = 1 \qquad\qquad log_{x^k} x = \frac{1}{x}\, log_a x \,, for\ k \neq 0$$

$$log_a(x.y) = log_a x + log_a y \qquad\qquad log_a x = log_{a^c} x^c$$

$$log_a \frac{x}{y} = log_a x - log_a y \qquad\qquad log_a x = \frac{1}{log_x a}$$

Examples:

Example 1. Expand this logarithm. $log_a (7 \times 4) =$

Solution: Use log rule: $log_a(x.y) = log_a x + log_a y$
Then: $log_a (7 \times 4) = log_a 7 + log_a 4$

Example 2. Condense this expression to a single logarithm. $log_a 5 - log_a 8$

Solution: Use log rule: $log_a x - log_a y = log_a \frac{x}{y}$
Then: $log_a 5 - log_a 8 = log_a \frac{5}{8}$

Example 3. Expand this logarithm. $log \left(\frac{1}{9}\right) =$

Solution: Use log rule: $log_a \frac{1}{x} = -log_a x$

Then: $log \left(\frac{1}{9}\right) = -log\ 9$

Natural Logarithms

☆ A natural logarithm is a logarithm that has a special base of the mathematical constant e, which is an irrational number approximately equal to 2.71.

☆ The natural logarithm of x is generally written as $ln\ x$, or $log_e x$.

Examples:

Example 1. Expand this natural logarithm. $ln\ 6x^2 =$

Solution: Use log rule: $log_a(x \cdot y) = log_a x + log_a y$
Then: $ln\ 6x^2 = ln\ 6 + ln\ x^2$. Now, use log rule: $log_a(M)^k = k.log_a(M) \rightarrow$
$ln\ 6 + ln\ x^2 = ln\ 6 + 2\ ln\ x$

Example 2. Condense this expression to a single logarithm. $ln\ 2x - log_e 3y$

Solution: Use log rule: $log_a x - log_a y = log_a \frac{x}{y}$
Then: $ln\ 2x - log_e 3y = ln\frac{2x}{3y}$

Example 3. Solve this equation for x: $e^x = 8$

Solution: If $f(x) = g(x)$, then: $ln(f(x)) = ln(g(x)) \rightarrow ln(e^x) = ln(8)$
Use log rule: $log_a x^b = b\ log_a x \rightarrow ln(e^x) = x\ ln(e) \rightarrow x ln(e) = ln(8)$
$ln(e) = 1$, then: $x = ln(8)$

Example 4. Solve this equation for x: $ln(6x - 2) = 1$

Solution: Use log rule: $a = log_b(b^a) \rightarrow 1 = ln(e^1) = ln(e) \rightarrow ln(6x - 2) = ln\ (e)$
When the logs have the same base: $log_b(f(x)) = log_b(g(x)) \rightarrow f(x) = g(x)$

$ln(6x - 2) = ln(e)$, then: $6x - 2 = e \rightarrow x = \frac{e+2}{6}$

Solving Logarithmic Equations

To solve a logarithm equation:

☆ Convert the logarithmic equation to an exponential equation when it's possible. (If no base is indicated, the base of the logarithm is 10)

☆ Condense logarithms if you have more than one log on one side of the equation.

☆ Plug in the answers back into the original equation and check to see if the solution works.

Examples:

Example 1. Find the value of x in this equation. $log(6x + 3) = log(4x - 2)$

Solution: When the logs have the same base: $f(x) = g(x)$, then:
$\ln(f(x)) = \ln(g(x))$, $log(6x + 3) = log(4x - 2) \rightarrow 6x + 3 = 4x - 2 \rightarrow$
$6x + 3 - 4x + 2 = 0 \rightarrow 2x + 5 = 0 \rightarrow 2x = -5 \rightarrow x = -\frac{5}{2}$

Verify Solution: $log(6x + 3) = log(6(-\frac{5}{2}) + 3) = log(-12)$

Logarithms of negative numbers are not defined. Therefore, there is no solution for this equation

Example 2. Find the value of x in this equation. $log_2(36 - x^2) = 4$

Solution: Use log rule: $log_b x = log_b y$, then: $x = y$
We can write number 4 as a logarithm: $4 = log_2(2^4)$
Then: $log_2(36 - x^2) = log_2(2^4) \rightarrow log_2(36 - x^2) = log_2 16$
Then: $36 - x^2 = 16 \rightarrow 36 - 16 = x^2 \rightarrow x^2 = 20 \rightarrow x = \pm\sqrt{20} = \pm 2\sqrt{5}$
You can plug in back the solutions into the original equation to check your answer. $x = \sqrt{20} \rightarrow log_2(36 - \sqrt{20}^2) = 4 \rightarrow log_2(36 - 20) = 4 \rightarrow log_2 16 = 4$
$x = -\sqrt{20} \rightarrow log_2(36 - (-\sqrt{20})^2) = 4 \rightarrow log_2(36 - 20) = 4 \rightarrow log_2 16 = 4$
Both solutions work in the original equation.

Find more at

Day 25: Practices

✎ **Evaluate each logarithm.**

1) $2log_7(7) =$

2) $6log_2(8) =$

3) $2log_5(125) =$

4) $log_{100}(1) =$

5) $log_6(216) =$

6) $3log_4(16) =$

7) $\frac{1}{2}log_3(81) =$

8) $log_7(343) =$

✎ **Expand each logarithm.**

9) $log_b(5 \times 9) =$

10) $log_b(5 \times 7) =$

11) $log_b(xy) =$

12) $2\,log_b(xy)$

13) $log_b(2x^2 \times 3y) =$

14) $log\left(\frac{1}{7}\right) =$

✎ **Reduce the following expressions to simplest form.**

15) $e^x = 9$

16) $e^{ln4+ln5} =$

17) $e^{ln\left(\frac{9}{e}\right)} =$

18) $e^{ln2+ln7} =$

19) $6\,ln\left(e^5\right) =$

20) $ln(2x + 4) = 1$

✎ **Find the value of the variables in each equation.**

21) $log3x = log\,(x + 1) \rightarrow x =$ _____

22) $log(2x - 1) = log(4x - 2) \rightarrow x =$ _____

23) $log(6x + 1) = log(x + 3) \rightarrow x =$ _____

Effortless
Math
Education

Day 25: Answers

1) 2

2) 18

3) 6

4) 0

5) 3

6) 6

7) 2

8) 3

9) $log_b 5 + 2log_b 3$

10) $log_b 5 + log_b 7$

11) $log_b x + log_b y$

12) $2log_b x + 2log_b y$

13) $log_b 2 + log_b x^2 + log_b 3 + log_b y$

14) $-log\,7$

15) $2ln3$

16) 20

17) $\dfrac{9}{e}$

18) 14

19) 30

20) $\dfrac{e-4}{2}$

21) $x = \dfrac{1}{2}$

22) $x = \dfrac{1}{2}$

23) $x = \dfrac{2}{5}$

www.EffortlessMath.com

Effortless Math Education

DAY 26 Circles

Math topics that you'll learn in this chapter:

1. Circumference and Area of Circles
2. Arc length and sector Area
3. Equation of a Circle
4. Finding the Center and the Radius of Circles

177

Circumference and Area of Circles

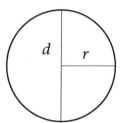

☆ In a circle, variable r is usually used for the radius and d for diameter.

☆ Area of a circle $= \pi r^2$ (π is about 3.14)

☆ Circumference of a circle $= 2\pi r$

Examples:

Example 1. Find the area of this circle.

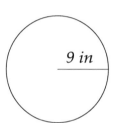

Solution:

Use area formula: $Area = \pi r^2$

$r = 9\ in \rightarrow Area = \pi(9)^2 = 81\pi,\ \pi = 3.14$

Then: $Area = 81 \times 3.14 = 254.34\ in^2$

Example 2. Find the Circumference of this circle.

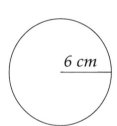

Solution:

Use Circumference formula: $Circumference = 2\pi r$

$r = 6\ cm \rightarrow Circumference = 2\pi(6) = 12\pi$

$\pi = 3.14$ Then: $Circumference = 12 \times 3.14 = 37.68\ cm$

Example 3. Find the Area of the circle.

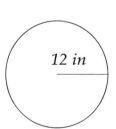

Solution:

Use area formula: $Area = \pi r^2$,

$r = 12\ in$, then: $Area = \pi(12)^2 = 144\pi,\ \pi = 3.14$

Then: $Area = 144 \times 3.14 = 452.16\ in^2$

bit.ly/3nWFuRC

Find more at

Arc Length and Sector Area

☆ To find the area of a sector of a circle, use this formula:

Area of a sector $= \pi r^2(\frac{\theta}{360})$, r is the radius of the circle and θ is the central angle of the sector.

☆ To find the arc of a sector of a circle, use this formula:

Arc of a sector $= (\frac{\theta}{180})\pi r$

Examples:

Example 1. Find the length of the arc. Round your answers to the nearest tenth.

$$(\pi = 3.14), r = 18 \ cm, \theta = 60°$$

Solution: Use this formula: Length of the sector $= \left(\frac{\theta}{180}\right)\pi r =$

$\left(\frac{60}{180}\right)\pi(18) = \left(\frac{1}{3}\right)\pi(18) = \left(\frac{18}{3}\right) \times 3.14 = 6 \times 3.14 = 18.84 \ cm$

Example 2. Find the area of the sector. $(\pi = 3.14)$ r = 8 ft, $\theta = 80°$

Solution: Use this formula: area of a sector $= \pi r^2(\frac{\theta}{360})$

Area of the sector $= \pi r^2 \left(\frac{\theta}{360}\right) = (3.14)(8^2) \left(\frac{80}{360}\right) = (3.14)(64)\left(\frac{2}{9}\right) =$
$200.96\left(\frac{2}{9}\right) = \frac{401.92}{9} \cong 44.66 \ ft^2$

Example 3. Find the length of the arc. $(\pi = 3.14)$ r = 4 ft, $\theta = \frac{\pi}{4}$

Solution: $\theta = \frac{\pi}{4} \rightarrow \frac{\pi}{4} \times \frac{180}{\pi} = 45°$

Length of the sector $= \left(\frac{45}{180}\right)\pi(4) = \left(\frac{1}{4}\right)\pi(4) = 1 \times 3.14 = 3.14 \ cm$

Equation of a Circle

⭐ Equation of circles in standard form: $(x - h)^2 + (y - k)^2 = r^2$

   Center: (h, k), Radius: r

⭐ Equation of circles in general form: $x^2 + y^2 + Ax + By + C = 0$

Examples:

Write the standard form equation of each circle.

Example 1. The center of the circle is at $(-3, -8)$, and its radius is 4.

Solution: $(x - h)^2 + (y - k)^2 = r^2$ is the circle equation with a radius r, centered at (h, k). So, $h = -3$, $k = -8$ and $r = 4$

Then, the equation of the circle is: $(x - (-3))^2 + (y - (-8))^2 = (4)^2 \rightarrow$
$(x + 3)^2 + (y + 8)^2 = (4)^2$

Example 2. $x^2 + y^2 + 4x - 6y - 3 = 0$

Solution: The standard form of circle equation is: $(x - h)^2 + (y - k)^2 = r^2$ where the radius of the circle is r, and it's centered at (h, k).

First, move the loose number to the right side: $x^2 + y^2 + 4x - 6y = 3$

Group x −variables and y −variables together: $(x^2 + 4x) + (y^2 - 6y) = 3$

Convert x to square form:

$(x^2 + 4x + 4) + y^2 - 6y = 3 + 4 \rightarrow (x + 2)^2 + (y^2 - 6y) = 3 + 4$

Convert y to square form:

$(x + 2)^2 + (y^2 - 6y + 9) = 3 + 4 + 9 \rightarrow (x - 2)^2 + (y - 3)^2 = 16$

Then, the equation of the circle in standard form is:

$(x + 2)^2 + (y - 3)^2 = 4^2$

bit.ly/3tSpuSs

Find more at

Finding the Center and the Radius of Circles

To find the center and the radius of a circle using the equation of the circle:

☆ Write the equation of the circle in standard form: $(x - h)^2 + (y - k)^2 = r^2$,

☆ The center of the circle is at (h, k), and its radius is r.

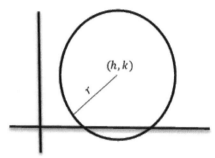

Examples:

Identify the center and the radius of each circle:

Example 1. Solve: $x^2 + y^2 - 4x + 3 = 0$

Solution: $(x - h)^2 + (y - k)^2 = r^2$ is the circle equation with a radius r, centered at (h, k).

Rewrite $x^2 + y^2 - 4x + 3 = 0$ in the standard form:

$x^2 + y^2 - 4x + 3 = 0 \rightarrow (x - 2)^2 + y^2 = 1^2$

Then, the center is at: $(2, 0)$ and $r = 1$

Example 2. Solve: $8x + x^2 + 10y = 8 - y^2$

Solution: Rewrite the equation in standard form:

$8x + x^2 + 10y = 8 - y^2 \rightarrow (x - (-4))^2 + (y - (-5))^2 = 7^2$

Then, the center is at $(-4, -5)$ and the radius is 7.

Day 26: Practices

✎ **Complete the table below.** ($\pi = 3.14$)

1)

	Radius	Diameter	Circumference	Area
Circle 1	3 inches	6 inches	18.84 inches	28.26 square inches
Circle 2			37.68 meters	
Circle 3		4 ft		
Circle 4				50.24 square miles

✎ **Find the length of each arc. Round your answers to the nearest hundredth.**

2) $r = 12 \, \text{cm}, \theta = 85° \rightarrow \text{arc} =$

3) $r = 15 \, \text{ft}, \theta = 95° \rightarrow \text{arc} =$

4) $r = 22 \, \text{ft}, \theta = 60° \rightarrow \text{arc} =$

5) $r = 28 \, \text{cm}, \theta = 45° \rightarrow \text{arc} =$

✎ **Write the standard form equation of each circle.**

6) $x^2 + y^2 - 4x + 2y - 4 = 0 \rightarrow$

7) $x^2 + y^2 - 8x + 6y - 11 = 0 \rightarrow$

8) $x^2 + y^2 - 10x - 12y + 12 = 0 \rightarrow$

9) $x^2 + y^2 + 12x - 6y - 19 = 0 \rightarrow$

10) $x^2 + y^2 - 6x + 8y + 24 = 0 \rightarrow$

✎ **Identify the center and radius of each circle.**

11) $(x + 1)^2 + (y - 2)^2 = 25 \rightarrow$ Center: (___,___) Radius: _____

12) $(x - 5)^2 + (y + 10)^2 = 4 \rightarrow$ Center: (___,___) Radius: _____

13) $x^2 + (y - 3)^2 = 64 \rightarrow$ Center: (___,___) Radius: _____

14) $(x - 1)^2 + y^2 = 9 \rightarrow$ Center: (___,___) Radius: _____

15) $x^2 + y^2 = 16 \rightarrow$ Center: (___,___) Radius: _____

Effortless
Math
Education

Day 26: Answers

1)

	Radius	Diameter	Circumference	Area
Circle 1	3 inches	6 inches	18.84 inches	28.26 square inches
Circle 2	6 meters	12 meters	37.68 meters	113.04 square meters
Circle 3	2 ft	4 ft	12.56 ft	12.56 square ft
Circle 4	4 miles	8 miles	25.12 miles	50.24 square miles

2) 17.80

3) 24.90

4) 23.03

5) 22

6) $(x - 2)^2 + (y - (-1))^2 = 3^2$

7) $(x - 4)^2 + (y - (-3))^2 = 6^2$

8) $(x - 5)^2 + (y - 6)^2 = 7^2$

9) $(x - (-6))^2 + (y - 3)^2 = 8^2$

10) $(x - 3)^2 + (y - (-4))^2 = 1^2$

11) Center: $(-1, 2)$, Radius: 5

12) Center: $(5, -10)$, Radius: 2

13) Center: $(0, 3)$, Radius: 8

14) Center: $(1, 0)$, Radius: 3

15) Center: $(0, 0)$, Radius: 4

Effortless Math Education

DAY 27 Rational Expressions

Math topics that you'll learn in this chapter:

1. Simplifying Complex Fractions

2. Graphing Rational Expressions

3. Adding and Subtracting Rational Expressions

185

Simplifying Complex Fractions

✩ Convert mixed numbers to improper fractions.

✩ Simplify all fractions.

✩ Write the fraction in the numerator of the main fraction line then write division sign (÷) and the fraction of the denominator.

✩ Use normal method for dividing fractions.

✩ Simplify as needed.

Example:

Example 1. Simplify: $\dfrac{\frac{3}{4}}{\frac{3}{22}-\frac{5}{18}}$

Solution: First, simplify the denominator: $\dfrac{3}{22}-\dfrac{5}{18}=-\dfrac{14}{99}$,

Then: $\dfrac{\frac{3}{4}}{\frac{3}{22}-\frac{5}{18}}=\dfrac{\frac{3}{4}}{-\frac{14}{99}}$; Now, write the complex fraction using the division sign:

$\dfrac{\frac{3}{4}}{-\frac{14}{99}}=\dfrac{3}{4}\div\left(-\dfrac{14}{99}\right)$. Use the dividing fractions rule: Keep, Change, Flip (keep the

first fraction, change the division sign to multiplication, flip the second fraction)

$\dfrac{3}{4}\div\left(-\dfrac{14}{99}\right)=\dfrac{3}{4}\times\left(-\dfrac{99}{14}\right)=-\dfrac{297}{56}$

Example 2. Simplify: $\dfrac{\frac{2}{7}\div\frac{1}{4}}{\frac{7}{8}+\frac{1}{4}}$

Solution: First, simplify the numerator: $\dfrac{2}{7}\div\dfrac{1}{4}=\dfrac{8}{7}$, then, simplify the

denominator: $\dfrac{7}{8}+\dfrac{1}{4}=\dfrac{9}{8}$, Now, write the complex fraction using the division

sign (÷): $\dfrac{\frac{2}{7}\div\frac{1}{4}}{\frac{7}{8}+\frac{1}{4}}=\dfrac{\frac{8}{7}}{\frac{9}{8}}=\dfrac{8}{7}\div\dfrac{9}{8}$, Use the dividing fractions rule:

(Keep, Change, Flip) $\dfrac{8}{7}\div\dfrac{9}{8}=\dfrac{8}{7}\times\dfrac{8}{9}=\dfrac{64}{63}=1\dfrac{1}{63}$

Graphing Rational Expressions

✫ A rational expression is a fraction in which the numerator and/or the denominator are polynomials. Examples: $\frac{1}{x}, \frac{x^2}{x-1}, \frac{x^2-x+2}{x^2+5x+1}, \frac{m^2+6m-5}{m-2m}$

✫ To graph a rational function:

   o Find the vertical asymptotes of the function if there is any. (Vertical asymptotes are vertical lines which correspond to the zeroes of the denominator. The graph will have a vertical asymptote at $x = a$ if the denominator is zero at $x = a$ and the numerator isn't zero at $x = a$)

   o Find the horizontal or slant asymptote. (If the numerator has a bigger degree than the denominator, there will be a slant asymptote. To find the slant asymptote, divide the numerator by the denominator using either long division or synthetic division.)

   o If the denominator has a bigger degree than the numerator, the horizontal asymptote is the x −axes or the line $y = 0$. If they have the same degree, the horizontal asymptote equals the leading coefficient (the coefficient of the largest exponent) of the numerator divided by the leading coefficient of the denominator.

   o Find intercepts and plug in some values of x and solve for y, then graph the function.

Example:

Example 1. Graph rational function. $f(x) = \frac{x^2-x+2}{x-1}$

Solution: First, notice that the graph is in two pieces. Most rational functions have graphs in multiple pieces. Find $y-$ intercept by substituting zero for x and solving for y ($f(x)$): $x = 0 \rightarrow y = \frac{x^2-x+2}{x-1} = \frac{0^2-0+2}{0-1} = -2$,

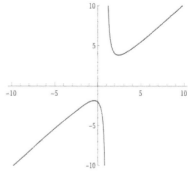

$y-$ intercept: $(0, -2)$ Asymptotes of $\frac{x^2-x+2}{x-1}$: Vertical: $x = 1$, Slant asymptote: $y = 2x + 1$ (divide the numerator by the denominator). After finding the asymptotes, you can plug in some values for x and solve for y. Here is the sketch for this function.

Adding and Subtracting Rational Expressions

For adding and subtracting rational expressions:

☆ Find least common denominator (LCD).

☆ Write each expression using the LCD.

☆ Add or subtract the numerators.

☆ Simplify as needed.

Examples:

Example 1. Solve. $\frac{5}{x+4} + \frac{x-3}{x+4} =$

Solution: The denominators are equal. Then, use fractions addition rule:

$$\frac{a}{c} \pm \frac{b}{c} = \frac{a \pm b}{c} \rightarrow \frac{5}{x+4} + \frac{x-3}{x+4} = \frac{5+(x-3)}{x+4} = \frac{x+2}{x+4}$$

Example 2. Solve. $\frac{x+2}{x-4} + \frac{x-2}{x+5} =$

Solution: Find the least common denominator of $(x-5)$ and $(x+6)$: $(x-5)(x+6)$

Then: $\frac{x+2}{x-4} + \frac{x-2}{x+5} = \frac{(x+2)(x+5)}{(x-4)(x+5)} + \frac{(x-2)(x-4)}{(x-4)(x+5)} = \frac{(x+2)(x+5)+(x-2)(x-4)}{(x-4)(x+5)}$

Expand: $(x+2)(x+5) + (x-2)(x-4) = 2x^2 + x + 18$

Then: $\frac{(x+2)(x+5)+(x-2)(x-4)}{(x-4)(x+5)} = \frac{2x^2+x+18}{(x-4)(x+5)} = \frac{2x^2+x+18}{x^2+x-20}$

Day 27: Practices

✍ Simplify each expression.

1) $\dfrac{\frac{3}{7}}{\frac{4}{9}} =$

3) $\dfrac{\frac{6}{7} \cdot \frac{1}{4}}{\frac{3}{5} + \frac{1}{3}} =$

2) $\dfrac{4}{\frac{5}{9} + \frac{2}{5}} =$

4) $\dfrac{x}{\frac{3}{4} - \frac{5}{x}} =$

✍ Graph rational expressions.

5) $f(x) = \dfrac{x^2}{2x+1}$

6) $f(x) = \dfrac{x^2+2x+6}{x+2}$

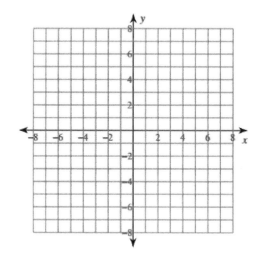

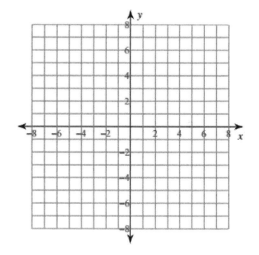

✍ Simplify each expression.

7) $\dfrac{3}{x+3} + \dfrac{x-2}{x+3} =$

9) $\dfrac{6}{2x+5} + \dfrac{x-5}{x+10} =$

8) $\dfrac{5}{x+4} - \dfrac{8}{x+5} =$

10) $\dfrac{3}{2x+6} - \dfrac{x-4}{x+3} =$

Day 27: Answers

1) $\dfrac{27}{28}$

2) $\dfrac{180}{43}$

3) $\dfrac{180}{49}$

4) $\dfrac{4x^2}{3x-20}$

5)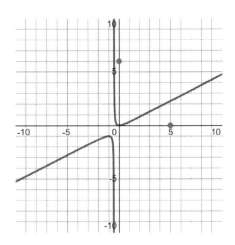

6)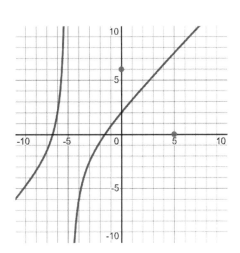

7) $\dfrac{x+1}{x+3}$

8) $\dfrac{-3x-7}{(x+4)(x+5)}$

9) $\dfrac{2x^2+x+35}{(2x+5)(x+10)}$

10) $\dfrac{-2x+11}{2(x+3)}$

Effortless Math Education

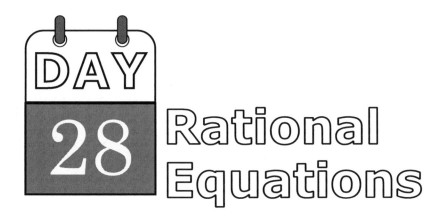

DAY 28 Rational Equations

Math topics that you'll learn in this chapter:

1. Multiplying Rational Expressions

2. Dividing Rational Expressions

3. Rational Equations

191

Multiplying Rational Expressions

☆ Multiplying rational expressions is the same as multiplying fractions. First, multiply numerators and then multiply denominators. Then, simplify as needed.

Examples:

Example 1. Solve: $\frac{x+3}{x-2} \times \frac{x-2}{4} =$

Solution: Multiply numerators and denominators: $\frac{a}{b} \times \frac{c}{d} = \frac{a \times c}{b \times d}$

$$\frac{x+3}{x-2} \times \frac{x-2}{4} = \frac{(x+3)(x-2)}{4(x-2)}$$

Cancel the common factor: $(x-2)$

Then: $\frac{(x+3)(x-2)}{4(x-2)} = \frac{(x+3)}{4}$

Example 2. Solve: $\frac{x-4}{x+5} \times \frac{2x+10}{x-2} =$

Solution: Multiply numerators and denominators:

$$\frac{x-4}{x+5} \times \frac{2x+10}{x-2} = \frac{x-4}{x+5} \times \frac{2(x+5)}{x-2} = \frac{2(x-4)(x+5)}{(x+5)(x-2)}$$

Cancel the common factor: $\frac{2(x-4)(x+5)}{(x+5)(x-2)} = \frac{2(x-4)}{(x-2)} = \frac{2x-8}{(x-2)}$

bit.ly/3fclilU

Find more at

Dividing Rational Expressions

✰ To divide rational expressions, use the same method we use for dividing fractions. (Keep, Change, Flip)

✰ Keep the first rational expression, change the division sign to multiplication, and flip the numerator and denominator of the second rational expression. Then, multiply numerators and multiply denominators. Simplify as needed.

Examples:

Example 1. Solve. $\frac{x+3}{x} \div \frac{x^2+x+5}{x^2+2x} =$

Solution: Use fractions division rule: $\frac{a}{b} \div \frac{c}{d} = \frac{a}{b} \times \frac{d}{c} = \frac{a \times d}{b \times c}$

$$\frac{x+3}{x} \div \frac{x^2+x+5}{x^2+2x} = \frac{x+3}{x} \times \frac{x^2+2x}{x^2+x+5} = \frac{(x+3)(x^2+2x)}{(x)(x^2+x+5)}$$

Now, factorize the expressions $x^2 + 2x$. Then:

$$x^2 + 2x = x(x+2)$$

Simplify: $\frac{(x+3)(x^2+2x)}{(x)(x^2+x+5)} = \frac{(x+3)(x)(x+2)}{(x)(x^2+x+5))}$, cancel common factors. Then:

$$\frac{(x+3)(x)(x+2)}{(x)(x^2+x+5))} = \frac{(x+3)(x+2)}{(x^2+x+5))}$$

Example 2. Solve. $\frac{7x}{x+5} \div \frac{x}{4x+8} =$

Solution: Use fractions division rule: $\frac{a}{b} \div \frac{c}{d} = \frac{a}{b} \times \frac{d}{c} = \frac{a \times d}{b \times c}$

Then: $\frac{7x}{x+5} \div \frac{x}{4x+8} = \frac{7x}{x+5} \times \frac{4x+8}{x} = \frac{7x(4x+8)}{x(x+5)} = \frac{7x \times 2(x+4)}{x(x+5)}$

Cancel common factor: $\frac{7x \times 2(x+4)}{x(x+5)} = \frac{14x(x+4)}{x(x+5)} = \frac{14(x+4)}{(x+5)}$

Rational Equations

For solving rational equations, we can use following methods:

☆ **Converting to a common denominator:** In this method, you need to get a common denominator for both sides of the equation. Then, make numerators equal and solve for the variable.

☆ **Cross-multiplying:** This method is useful when there is only one fraction on each side of the equation. Simply multiply the first numerator by the second denominator and make the result equal to the product of the second numerator and the first denominator.

Examples:

Example 1. Solve. $\frac{2x}{x-3} = \frac{2x+2}{2x-6}$

Solution: Multiply the numerator and denominator of the rational expression on the left by 2 to get a common denominator $(2x - 6)$. $\frac{2(2x)}{2(x-3)} = \frac{4x}{2x-6}$

Now, the denominators on both side of the equation are equal. Therefore, their numerators must be equal too.

$$\frac{4x}{2x-6} = \frac{2x+2}{2x-6} \rightarrow 4x = 2x + 2 \rightarrow 2x = 2 \rightarrow x = 1$$

Example 2. Solve. $\frac{x-3}{x+1} = \frac{x+5}{x-3}$

Solution: Use cross multiply method: if $\frac{a}{b} = \frac{c}{d}$, then: $a \times d = b \times c$

$\frac{x-3}{x+1} = \frac{x+5}{x-3} \rightarrow (x-3)(x-3) = (x+5)(x+1)$

Expand: $(x-3)^2 = x^2 - 6x + 9$ and $(x+5)(x+1) = x^2 + 6x + 5$,

Then: $x^2 - 6x + 9 = x^2 + 6x + 5$, Now, subtract both sides (-5), $x^2 - 6x + 9 - 5 = x^2 + 6x + 5 - 5 \rightarrow x^2 - 6x + 4 = x^2 + 6x$

subtract both sides $(x^2 + 6x)$

Then: $x^2 - 6x + 4 - (x^2 + 6x) = x^2 + 6x - (x^2 + 6x) \rightarrow -12x + 4 = 0$
$\rightarrow x = \frac{4}{12} = \frac{1}{3}$

bit.ly/3cgj6OP

Find more at

Day 28: Practices

✎ Simplify each expression.

1) $\dfrac{x+1}{x+2} \times \dfrac{x+3}{x+1} =$

2) $\dfrac{x+3}{x} \times \dfrac{9}{x+3} =$

3) $\dfrac{x+3}{x} \times \dfrac{2}{x+4} =$

4) $\dfrac{x+9}{x+1} \times \dfrac{x^2}{x+9} =$

5) $\dfrac{x-3}{x+2} \times \dfrac{2x+4}{x+4} =$

6) $\dfrac{x-6}{x+3} \times \dfrac{2x+6}{2x} =$

✎ Solve.

7) $\dfrac{3x}{4} \div \dfrac{3}{2} =$

8) $\dfrac{6}{3x} \div \dfrac{24}{x} =$

9) $\dfrac{3x}{x+4} \div \dfrac{x}{3x+12} =$

10) $\dfrac{5}{2x} \div \dfrac{16}{10x} =$

11) $\dfrac{36x}{5} \div \dfrac{4}{3} =$

12) $\dfrac{16x^2}{6} \div \dfrac{8x}{14} =$

✎ Solve each equation.

13) $\dfrac{2x-2}{x-2} = \dfrac{x+2}{x-2} \rightarrow x = \underline{\qquad}$

14) $\dfrac{x+6}{x+2} = \dfrac{x+5}{x+6} \rightarrow x = \underline{\qquad}$

15) $\dfrac{1}{8x^2} = \dfrac{1}{4x^2} - \dfrac{1}{x} \rightarrow x = \underline{\qquad}$

16) $\dfrac{1}{x} + \dfrac{1}{9x} = \dfrac{5}{36} \rightarrow x = \underline{\qquad}$

17) $\dfrac{32}{2x^2} + 1 = \dfrac{8}{x} \rightarrow x = \underline{\qquad}$

18) $\dfrac{1}{x-5} = \dfrac{4}{x-5} + 1 \rightarrow x = \underline{\qquad}$

Day 28: Answers

1) $\dfrac{x+3}{x+2}$

2) $\dfrac{9}{x}$

3) $\dfrac{2(x+3)}{x(x+4)}$

4) $\dfrac{x^2}{x+1}$

5) $\dfrac{2(x-3)}{x+4}$

6) $\dfrac{x-6}{x}$

7) $\dfrac{x}{2}$

8) $\dfrac{1}{12}$

9) 9

10) $\dfrac{25}{16}$

11) $\dfrac{27x}{5}$

12) $\dfrac{14x}{3}$

13) $x = 4$

14) $x = -\dfrac{26}{5}$

15) $x = \dfrac{1}{8}$

16) $x = 8$

17) $x = 4$

18) $x = 2$

**Effortless
Math
Education**

DAY 29 Trigonometric Functions

Math topics that you'll learn in this chapter:

1. Angle and Angle Measure
2. Trigonometric Functions
3. Coterminal Angles and Reference Angles

197

Angle and Angle Measure

✰ To convert degrees to radians, use this formula:

$$\text{Radians} = \text{Degrees} \times \frac{\pi}{180}$$

✰ To convert radians to degrees, use this formula:

$$\text{Degrees} = \text{Radians} \times \frac{180}{\pi}$$

Examples:

Example 1. Convert 120 degrees to radian.

Solution: Use this formula: $\text{Radians} = \text{Degrees} \times \frac{\pi}{180}$

$\text{Radians} = 120 \times \frac{\pi}{180} = \frac{120\pi}{180} = \frac{2\pi}{3}$

Example 2. Convert radian measure $\frac{\pi}{4}$ to degree measure.

Solution: Use this formula: $\text{Degrees} = \text{Radians} \times \frac{180}{\pi}$

$\text{Radians} = \frac{\pi}{4} \times \frac{180}{\pi} = \frac{180\pi}{4\pi} = 45$

Example 3. Convert 140 degrees to radian.

Solution: Use this formula: $\text{Radians} = \text{Degrees} \times \frac{\pi}{180}$

$\text{Radians} = 140 \times \frac{\pi}{180} = \frac{140\pi}{180} = \frac{7\pi}{9}$

Example 4. Convert radian measure $\frac{3\pi}{4}$ to degree measure.

Solution: Use this formula: $\text{Degrees} = \text{Radians} \times \frac{180}{\pi}$

$\text{Radians} = \frac{3\pi}{4} \times \frac{180}{\pi} = \frac{540\pi}{4\pi} = 135$

bit.ly/3pxMlAh

Find more at

Trigonometric Functions

☆ Trigonometric functions refer to the relation between the sides and angles of a right triangle. There are 6 trigonometric functions:

☆ Sine (sin), Cosine (cos), Tangent (tan), Secant (sec), Cosecant (csc), and Cotangent (cot)

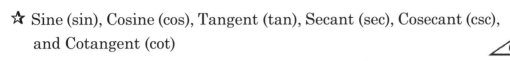

☆ The three main trigonometric functions:

$$SOH - CAH - TOA, \ sin\,\theta = \frac{opposite}{hypotenuse}, \ Cos\,\theta = \frac{adjacent}{hypotenuse}, \ tan\,\theta = \frac{opposite}{adjacent}$$

☆ The reciprocal trigonometric functions:

$$csc\,x = \frac{1}{sin\,x}, \ sec\,x = \frac{1}{cos\,x}, \ cot\,\theta = \frac{1}{tan\,x}$$

☆ Learn common trigonometric functions:

θ	0°	30°	45°	60°	90°
$\sin\theta$	0	$\frac{1}{2}$	$\frac{\sqrt{2}}{2}$	$\frac{\sqrt{3}}{2}$	1
$\cos\theta$	1	$\frac{\sqrt{3}}{2}$	$\frac{\sqrt{2}}{2}$	$\frac{1}{2}$	0
$\tan\theta$	0	$\frac{\sqrt{3}}{3}$	1	$\sqrt{3}$	Undefined

Examples:

Find each trigonometric function.

Example 1. $sin\,135°$

Solution: Use the following property: $sin(x) = cos(90° - x)$

$sin\,135° = cos(90° - 135°) = cos(-45°) = \frac{\sqrt{2}}{2}$

Coterminal Angles and Reference Angles

☆ Coterminal angles are equal angles.

☆ To find a Coterminal of an angle, add or subtract 360 degrees (or 2π for radians) to the given angle.

☆ Reference angle is the smallest angle that you can make from the terminal side of an angle with the x −axis.

Examples:

Example 1. Find a positive and a negative Coterminal angle to angle 55°.

Solution:

$55° - 360° = -305°$

$55° + 360° = 415°$

$-305°$ and a $415°$ are Coterminal with angle 55°.

Example 2. Find positive and negative Coterminal angles to angle $\frac{\pi}{3}$.

Solution:

$\frac{\pi}{3} + 2\pi = \frac{7\pi}{3}$

$\frac{\pi}{3} - 2\pi = -\frac{5\pi}{3}$

Example 3. Find a positive and a negative Coterminal angle to angle 85°.

Solution:

$85° - 360° = -275°$

$85° + 360° = 445°$

$-275°$ and a $445°$ are Coterminal with angle 80°.

Day 29: Practices

✍ Convert each degree measure into radians and radians into degree.

1) $90° =$

2) $120° =$

3) $140° =$

4) $92° =$

5) $\frac{3\pi}{2} =$

6) $\frac{3\pi}{5} =$

✍ Evaluate.

7) $\sin 60° =$ _____

8) $\sin -120° =$ _____

9) $\tan -30° =$ _____

10) $\cot \frac{\pi}{3} =$ _____

11) $\tan \frac{\pi}{3} =$ _____

12) $\sin \frac{2\pi}{6} =$ _____

✍ Find a positive and a negative Coterminal angle for each angle.

13) $60° =$

    Positive = _____

    Negative = _____

14) $-115° =$

    Positive = _____

    Negative = _____

15) $190° =$

    Positive = _____

    Negative = _____

16) $\frac{2\pi}{3} =$

    Positive = _____

    Negative = _____

Day 29: Answers

1) $\frac{\pi}{2}$

2) $\frac{2\pi}{3}$

3) $\frac{7\pi}{9}$

4) $\frac{23\pi}{45}$

5) $270°$

6) $108°$

7) $\frac{\sqrt{3}}{2}$

8) $-\frac{\sqrt{3}}{2}$

9) $-\frac{\sqrt{3}}{3}$

10) $\frac{\sqrt{3}}{3}$

11) $\sqrt{3}$

12) $\frac{\sqrt{3}}{2}$

13) $Positive = 420°$, $Negative = -300°$

14) $Positive = 245°$, $Negative = -475°$

15) $Positive = 550°$, $Negative = -170°$

16) $Positive = \frac{8\pi}{3}$, $Negative = -\frac{4\pi}{3}$

Effortless Math Education

DAY 30 Evaluating Trigonometric Functions

 Math topics that you'll learn in this chapter:

1. Evaluating Trigonometric Functions

2. Missing Sides and Angles of a Right Triangle

203

Evaluating Trigonometric Functions

☆ **Step 1:** Find the reference angle. (It is the smallest angle that you can make from the terminal side of an angle with the x−axis.)

☆ **Step 2:** Determine the quadrant of the function. Depending on the quadrant in which the function lies, the answer will be either positive or negative.

☆ **Step 3:** Find the trigonometric function of the reference angle.

Examples:

Example 1. Find the exact value of trigonometric function. $tan \frac{4\pi}{3}$

Solution: Rewrite the angle for $\frac{4\pi}{3}$:
$tan \frac{4\pi}{3} = tan \left(\frac{3\pi+\pi}{3}\right) = \tan \left(\pi + \frac{1}{3}\pi\right)$
Use the periodicity of tan: $tan(x + \pi . k) = tan(x)$
$tan \left(\pi + \frac{1}{3}\pi\right) = tan \left(\frac{1}{3}\pi\right) = \sqrt{3}$

Example 2. Find the exact value of trigonometric function. $cos\ 240°$

Solution: Write $cos\ (240°)$ as $cos\ (60° + 180°)$.
Recall that $\cos 60° = -\frac{1}{2}, \cos 90° = 0$
The reference angle of $240°$ is $90°$. Therefore, $cos\ 240° = -\frac{1}{2}$

Example 3. Find the exact value of trigonometric function. $sin \frac{7\pi}{6}$

Solution: Rewrite the $sin \frac{7\pi}{6}$.
$sin \frac{7\pi}{6} = sin \left(\frac{\pi}{6} + \pi\right) = -sin(\frac{\pi}{6})$

Trig Table of Special Arcs gives: $-sin\frac{\pi}{6} = -\frac{1}{2}$

bit.ly/3aUyyQy

Find more at

Missing Sides and Angles of a Right Triangle

☆ By using three main trigonometric functions (Sine, Cosine or Tangent), we can find an unknown side in a right triangle when we have one length, and one angle (apart from the right angle).

☆ A right triangle with Adjacent and Opposite sides and Hypotenuse is shown below.

☆ **Recall** the three main trigonometric functions:

SOH – CAH – TOA, $sin\,\theta = \frac{opposite}{hypotenuse}$, $Cos\,\theta = \frac{adjacent}{hypotenuse}$, $tan\,\theta = \frac{opposite}{adjacent}$

☆ To find missing angles, use inverse of trigonometric functions (examples: $sin^{-1}, cos^{-1},$ and tan^{-1})

Examples:

Example 1. Find side AC in the following triangle. Round your answer to the nearest tenth.

Solution: $sin\,\theta = \frac{opposite}{hypotenuse}$. $sine\,60° = \frac{AC}{6} \rightarrow 6 \times sin\,60° = AC$,

Now use a calculator to find $sine\,60°$.

$$sin\,60° \approx 0.866$$

$AC = 6 \times \frac{\sqrt{3}}{2} = 3\sqrt{3}$, rounding to the nearest tenth: $5.196 \approx 5.2$

Example 2. Find the value of x in the following triangle.

Solution: $cos\,\theta = \frac{adjacent}{hypotenuse} \rightarrow cos\,x = \frac{10}{14} = \frac{5}{7}$

Use a calculator to find inverse cosine:

$$cos^{-1}\left(\frac{5}{7}\right) = 44.41° \approx 44° \text{, Then: } x = 44$$

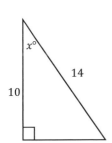

Day 30: Practices

✍ **Find the exact value of each trigonometric function.**

1) $cos\ 120° =$ _____

2) $sin\ -210° =$ _____

3) $tan\ 150° =$ _____

4) $sin\frac{\pi}{4} =$ _____

5) $csc\ 330° =$ _____

6) $cot\ -120° =$ _____

✍ **Find the value of x in each triangle. Round your answers to the nearest hundredth.**

7) _____

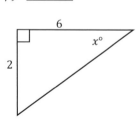

8) _____

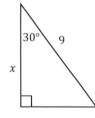

9) _____

10) _____

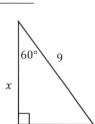

11) _____

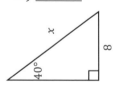

12) _____

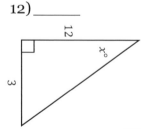

Effortless
Math
Education

Day 30: Answers

1) $-\frac{1}{2}$

2) $\frac{1}{2}$

3) $-\frac{\sqrt{3}}{3}$

4) $\frac{\sqrt{2}}{2}$

5) -2

6) $\frac{\sqrt{3}}{3}$

7) 18.43

8) 7.80

9) 63.43

10) 4.5

11) 12.40

12) 14

Effortless Math Education

Time to Test

Time to refine your skill with a practice examination

Take a REAL ALEKS Mathematics test to simulate the test day experience. After you've finished, score your test using the answers and explanations section.

Before You Start

- ❖ You'll need a pencil and scratch papers to take the test.
- ❖ For these practice tests, don't time yourself. Spend time as much as you need.
- ❖ After you've finished the test, review the answer key to see where you went wrong.

Good luck!

ALEKS Mathematics

Practice Test 1

2020 - 2021

Total number of questions: 35

Total time for two parts: <u>No time limit</u>

Calculators are permitted for ALEKS Math Test.

1) Evaluate.

$$18[26 - (1 + 3)^2]$$

$26 - (4)^2$

$26 - 16$

$16 \cdot 10 = 180$

2) Use a calculator to approximate $\sqrt{408}$.

Round your answer to the nearest hundredth.

$2\sqrt{102}$

3) Solve for x.

$$\frac{2x}{5} = 24$$

$x = 60$

$\frac{2}{24}$

$\cdot 5$

120

$x = 60$

$\frac{2x = 120}{2}$

4) Solve for a.

$$-3a + 8(a + 8) = 49$$

Simplify your answer as much as possible.

$-3a + 8a + 64 - 49 = 0$

$-3a + 8a + 15 = 0$

$-1(3 - 8a - 15) = 0$

12

$12 \quad ^{-8}_{-6} \quad _{-48}$

5) Factor completely.

$3x^2 - 18x + 24$

$3(x^2 - 6x + 8)$

$3(x-4)(x-2)$

6) Sketch the graph of inequality: $-8x < 16 - 4y$

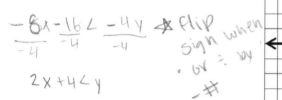

$-8x < 16 - 4y$
-16

$\dfrac{-8x}{-4} - \dfrac{16}{-4} < \dfrac{-4y}{-4}$ ✱ Flip sign when ÷ by -#

$2x + 4 < y$

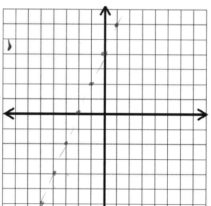

7) What is the area of a square whose diagonal is 6 cm?

$a^2 + b^2 = c^2$

$x^2 + x^2 = 6^2$

$\dfrac{2x^2}{2} = \dfrac{36}{2}$

$\sqrt{x^2} \sqrt{16}$

$x = \sqrt{18}$

$\sqrt{18} \cdot \sqrt{18} = 18\ cm^2$ ← area

8) What is the value of x in the following figure?

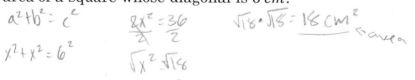

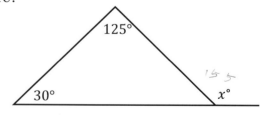

9) What is the value of y in the following system of equation?

$$3x - 4y = -20$$

$$3(-x + 2y = 20)$$

$$3x - 4y = -20$$
$$-3x + 6y = 60$$

$$\frac{2y = 40}{2} \quad y = 20$$

10) How long does a 384–miles trip take moving at 60 miles per hour (*mph*)?

6 hrs 24 ms

11) When 50% of 60 is added to 12% of 600, the resulting number is:

30   72

102

12) What is the solution of the following inequality?

$$|x - 10| \leq 4$$

$x \leq 14$

13) A bag contains 18 balls: two green, five black, eight blue, a brown, a red and one white. If 17 balls are removed from the bag at random, what is the probability that a brown ball has been removed?

$$\frac{\frac{17}{18}}{\frac{1}{17}} =$$

14) If a tree casts a 22–foot shadow at the same time that a 3 feet yardstick casts a 2–foot shadow, what is the height of the tree?

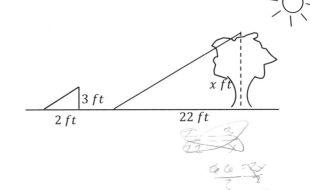

3 ft

2 ft   22 ft

$$\frac{2}{22} = \frac{3}{x}$$

$$\frac{66}{2} = \frac{2x}{2}$$

$$x = 33$$

15) What is the value of $\cos 30°$?

$$\frac{\sqrt{2}}{2}$$

16) Simplify. $2x^2 + 4y^5 - x^2 + 2z^3 - 2y^2 + 2x^3 - 2y^5 + 6z^3$

17) In five successive hours, a car traveled $40\ km, 45\ km, 50\ km, 35\ km$ and $55\ km$. In the next five hours, it traveled with an average speed of $65\ km\ per\ hour$. Find the total distance the car traveled in 10 hours.

550

18) From last year, the price of gasoline has increased from $1.40 per gallon to $1.75 per gallon. The new price is what percent of the original price?

19) 6 liters of water are poured into an aquarium that's 25 cm long, 5 cm wide, and 60 cm high. How many cm will the water level in the aquarium rise due to this added water? (1 $liter\ of\ water = 1,000\ cm^3$)

20) If a box contains red and blue balls in ratio of 2∶3, how many red balls are there if 75 blue balls are in the box?

50

21) A chemical solution contains 6% alcohol. If there is 24 ml of alcohol, what is the volume of the solution?

22) If $\frac{5x}{16} = \frac{x-1}{4}$, $x =$?

$20x = 16x - 16$

$-20x\ \ -20x$

$\frac{16}{-4} = \frac{-4x}{-4}$ $x = -4$

23) Simplify. $(-4 + 9i)(3 + 5i)$

$-12 - 20i + 21i + 45i^2$ $\quad (-1)$

$-57 + i$

24) If $\tan \theta = \frac{5}{12}$ and $\sin \theta > 0$, then $\cos \theta = ?$

$25 + 144$

169

25) What is the vertical asymptote of the graph $y = \frac{5x - 6}{3x + 4}$?

$3x + 4 = 0$

$\quad -4 \quad -4$

$x = -\frac{4}{3}$

$\frac{3x}{3} = \frac{-4}{3}$

26) A boat sails 80 miles south and then 60 miles east. How far is the boat from its start point?

100 mi

27) If $x \begin{bmatrix} 2 & 0 \\ 0 & 4 \end{bmatrix} = \begin{bmatrix} x + 3y - 5 & 0 \\ 0 & 2y + 10 \end{bmatrix}$, what is the product of x and y?

$2x = x + 3y - 5$

$+5 \quad -2x - 2y \quad +5$

$5 = -x + 3y$

$+10 = -4x + 2y$

$4x = 2y + 10$

$+4x \quad -10 \quad -4x$

-10

$-4(x - 3y = 5)$

$4x - 2y = 10$

$-4x + 12y = 20$

$4x - 2y = 10$

$10y =$

28) A number is chosen at random from 1 to 20. Find the probability of not selecting a composite number.

29) Removing which of the following numbers will change the average of the numbers to 8?

$$1, 4, 5, 8, 11, 12$$

30) If $y = 4ab + 3b^3$, what is the value of y, when $a = 2$ and $b = 4$?

$$4(2)(4) + 3(4)^3$$
$$32 + 192 = 224$$

31) Find the value of x in the following diagram. (there are 2 supplementary angles in the diagram)

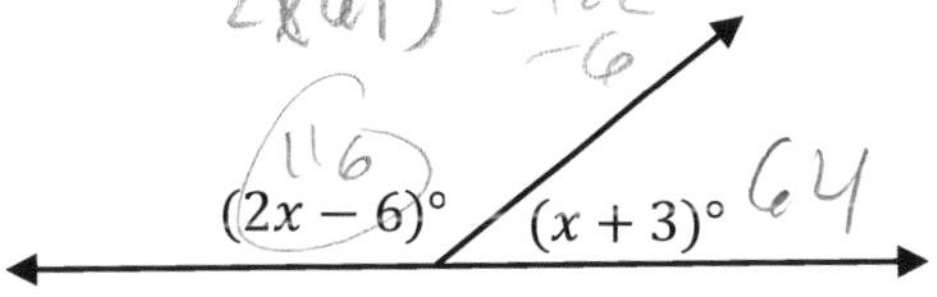

$$2x - 6 + x + 3 = 180$$
$$+6 \quad -3 \quad +6$$
$$\quad \quad -3$$
$$\frac{3x}{3} = \frac{183}{3}$$
$$x = 61$$

$$2(61) = 122$$
$$-6$$
$$116$$

$(2x - 6)°$ $(x + 3)°$ 64

32) Find the value of x in this equation. $log(5x + 2) = log(3x - 1)$

$$5x + 2 = 3x - 1$$
$$-3x + 1$$
$$2x + 3 = 0$$
$$\frac{2x}{2} = \frac{-3}{2}$$
$$x = -\frac{3}{2}$$

$$log(5(-\frac{3}{2}) + 2) = log(-5.5)$$

no sol

33) Solve for x: $ax - 8 = x + b$

34) Solve quadratic inequality. $x^2 - 2x - 15 \geq 0$

Graph the solution(s) and write the answer in interval format.

35) Find the domain and range of the radical function. $y = 3\sqrt{2x + 4} + 8$

Domain: _____

Range: _____

This is the end of Practice Test 1.

ALEKS Mathematics

Practice Test 2

2020 - 2021

Total number of questions: 35

Total time for two parts: <u>No time limit</u>

Calculators are permitted for ALEKS Math Test.

1) Solve for x.

   $7 = 18x - 7y$

2) Two trains leave the station at the same time, one heading west and the other east. The westbound train travels at 90 miles per hour. The eastbound train travels at 80 miles per hour. How long will it take for the two trains to be 425 miles apart?

3) Solve the inequality for x.

   $-6 + 2x > -4$

   Simplify your answer as much as possible.

4) Solve the following system of equations.

   $x + 2y = 10$

   $6x - 2y = 18$

5) Find the slope of the line passing through the points $(-4, 3)$ and $(-9, 7)$.

6) If $f(x) = -8x^2 + 12x$ and $g(x) = -2x + 3$, then find $(\frac{f}{g})(x)$.

7) A bank is offering 4.5% simple interest on a savings account. If you deposit $12,000, how much interest will you earn in two years?

8) If the ratio of home fans to visiting fans in a crowd is $3:2$ and all 24,000 seats in a stadium are filled, how many visiting fans are in attendance?

9) If the interior angles of a quadrilateral are in the ratio $2:3:3:4$, what is the measure of the largest angle?

10) If the area of a circle is 49 square meters, what is its radius?

11) The length of a rectangle is $\frac{5}{4}$ times its width. If the width is $20\ cm$, what is the perimeter of this rectangle?

12) In the figure below, line A is parallel to line B. What is the value of angle x?

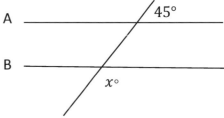

13) An angle is equal to one ninth of its supplement. What is the measure of that angle?

14) If $\frac{5}{x+1} = \frac{x+1}{x^2-1}$, then $x = $ ____

15) Last week 25,000 fans attended a football match. This week three times as many bought tickets, but one sixth of them cancelled their tickets. How many are attending this week?

16) If $sin\ A = \frac{1}{3}$ in a right triangle and the angle A is an acute angle, then what is $cos\ A$?

17) In the standard (x, y) coordinate system plane, what is the area of the circle with the following equation?

$$(x + 2)^2 + (y - 4)^2 = 25$$

18) Convert 580,000 to scientific notation.

19) The ratio of boys to girls in a school is $2:3$. If there are 500 students in a school, how many boys are in the school.

20) If 150% of a number is 75, then what is 80% of that number?

21) Find the center and the radius of a circle with the following equation.
$$x^2 + y^2 - 6x + 4y + 4 = 0$$

Center: (__, __)

radius = _____

22) What is the solution of the following inequality?

$$|x - 2| \geq 4$$

23) If $\tan x = \frac{8}{15}$, then $\sin x = ?$

24) $(x^6)^{\frac{7}{8}}$ equal to?

25) What are the zeroes of the function $f(x) = x^3 + 5x^2 + 6x$?

26) If $x + sin^2 a + cos^2 a = 3$, then $x = ?$

27) If $\sqrt{5x} = \sqrt{y}$, then $x =$

28) The average weight of 18 girls in a class is 55 kg and the average weight of 32 boys in the same class is 62 kg. What is the average weight of all the 50 students in that class?

29) What is the value of the expression $5(x - 2y) + (2 - x)^2$ when $x = 3$ and $y = -3$?

30) Sketch the graph of $y = (x + 1)^2 - 2$

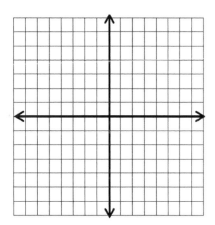

31) Simplify: $(8a - 6) + 4(a - 7) - 5(a + 3)$

32) Evaluate the expression $6x^2 - 2xy + y^2$, when $x = 3$ and $y = 7$.

33) Firefighters use the formula $S = 0.7P + 21$ to compute the horizontal range S in feet of water from a particular hose, where P is the nozzle pressure in pounds. Find the Horizontal range if the pressure is 120 lb.

34) Simplify this rational expression: $\dfrac{5x}{x+3} \div \dfrac{x}{2x+6} =$

35) Solve this equation for x: $e^{2x} = 12$

This is the end of Practice Test 2.

ALEKS Mathematics
Practice Tests Answers
and Explanations

ALEKS Mathematics Practice Test 1 Answers and Explanations

1) The answer is 180

Use order of operation rule PEMDAS. First, simplify inside the parenthesis:

$18[26 - (4)^2] \to 18[26 - 16] \to 18[10] = 180$

2) The answer is 20.20

Use a calculator and calculate $\sqrt{408}$. The answer is $20.1990098\ldots$

Rounding the answer to the nearest hundredth, the answer is 20.20

3) The answer is 60

To solve for the variable, isolate it on one side of the equation. For this equation, multiply both sides by 5. Then: $\frac{2x}{5} = 24 \to \frac{2x}{5} \times 5 = 24 \times 5 \to 2x = 120$

Now, divide both sides by 2. $x = \frac{120}{2} = 60$

4) The answer is $a = -3$

To solve for a, first use distributive property to simplify $8(a + 8)$. Then:

$8(a + 8) = 8a + 64$

Now, combine like terms: $-3a + 8(a + 8) = 49 \to -3a + 8a + 64 = 49 \to$

$5a + 64 = 49$

Subtract 64 from both sides: $5a + 64 - 64 = 49 - 64 \to 5a = -15 \to a = -3$

5) The answer is $3(x - 4)(x - 2)$

To factor this polynomial, first find the common factor and take it out from all terms. The common factor is 3. (the three terms $3x^2$, $-18x$ and 24 are divisible by 3)

$3x^2 - 18x + 24 = 3(x^2 - 6x + 8)$. To factorize $(x^2 - 6x + 8)$, we need to find two numbers whose sum is -6 and their product is 8. Those two numbers are -4 and -2. Then: $3(x^2 - 6x + 8) = 3(x - 4)(x - 2)$

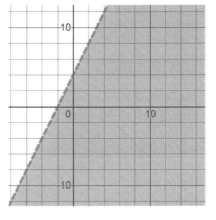

6) The answer is on the graph

To draw the graph of inequality $-8x < 16 - 4y$, first simplify the inequality and solve for y. Solving the inequality for y: Subtract 16 from both sides:

$-8x - 16 < 16 - 4y - 16 \rightarrow -8x - 16 < -4y$. Divide both sides by -4. (remember: For dividing or multiplying both sides by negative numbers, flip the direction of the inequality sign.)

$-8x - 16 < -4y \rightarrow \frac{-8x-16}{-4} > \frac{-4y}{-4} \rightarrow 2x + 4 > y$. Now, graph the inequality $2x + 4 > y$.

To draw the graph of $y < 2x + 4$, you first need to graph the line: $y = 2x + 4$

Since there is a less than ($<$) sign, draw a dash line. The slope is 2 and y-intercept is 4. Then, choose a testing point and substitute the value of x and y from that point into the inequality. The easiest point to test is the origin: $(0, 0)$

$(0,0) \rightarrow y < 2x + 4 \rightarrow 0 < 2(0) + 4 \rightarrow 0 < 4$

This is correct! 0 is less than 4. So, this part of the line (on the right side) is the solution of this inequality.

View the graph.

7) The answer is $18\ cm^2$

The diagonal of the square is $6\ cm$. Let x be the side.

Use Pythagorean Theorem: $a^2 + b^2 = c^2$

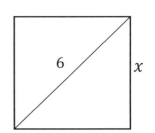

$$x^2 + x^2 = 6^2 \Rightarrow 2x^2 = 6^2 \Rightarrow 2x^2 = 36 \Rightarrow x^2 = 18 \Rightarrow x = \sqrt{18}$$

The area of the square is: $\sqrt{18} \times \sqrt{18} = 18 \ cm^2$

8) The answer is 155

The angle x equals to the sum of the two angles provided. Then:

$x = 30 + 125 = 155$

9) The answer is 20

Solve the system of equations by elimination method.

$$\begin{array}{l} 3x - 4y = -20 \\ \underline{-x + 2y = 20} \end{array}$$ Multiply the second equation by 3, then add it to the first

equation.

$$\begin{array}{l} 3x - 4y = -20 \\ \underline{3(-x + 2y = 20)} \end{array} \Rightarrow \begin{array}{l} 3x - 4y = -20 \\ \underline{-3x + 6y = 60)} \end{array} \Rightarrow \text{adding the equations: } 2y = 40 \Rightarrow y = 20$$

10) The answer is 6.4 hours

Use distance formula: $Distance = Rate \times time \Rightarrow 384 = 60 \times T$

Divide both sides by 60. $384 \div 60 = T \Rightarrow T = 6.4 \ hours$. Change hours to minutes for the decimal part. $0.4 \ hours = 0.4 \times 60 = 24 \ minutes$. The answer is 6 hours and 24 minutes or 6.4 hours.

11) The answer is 102

50% of 60 equals to: $0.50 \times 60 = 30$, 12% of 600 equals to: $0.12 \times 600 = 72$

50% of 60 added to 12% of 600: $30 + 72 = 102$

12) The answer is $6 \leq x \leq 14$

Since this inequality contains absolute value, then, the value inside absolute value bars is greater than -4 and less than 4. Then:

$$|x - 10| \leq 4 \rightarrow -4 \leq x - 10 \leq 4 \rightarrow -4 + 10 \leq x - 10 + 10 \leq 4 + 10 \rightarrow 6 \leq x \leq 14$$

13) The answer is $\frac{17}{18}$

If 17 balls are removed from the bag at random, there will be one ball in the bag. The probability of choosing a brown ball is 1 out of 18. Therefore, the probability of not choosing a brown ball is 17 out of 18 (or $\frac{17}{18}$) and the probability of having not a brown ball after removing 17 balls is the same.

14) The answer is 33 ft

Write a proportion and solve for x. $\frac{3}{2} = \frac{x}{22} \Rightarrow 2x = 3 \times 22 \Rightarrow x = 33 \, ft$

15) The answer is $\frac{\sqrt{3}}{2}$

The value of $cos \, 30° = \frac{\sqrt{3}}{2}$

16) The answer is $2x^3 + x^2 + 2y^5 - 2y^2 + 8z^3$

To simplify this polynomial, combine like terms. Then:

$2x^2 + 4y^5 - x^2 + 2z^3 - 2y^2 + 2x^3 - 2y^5 + 6z^3 =$

$2x^2 - x^2 + 2x^3 - 2y^2 + 4y^5 - 2y^5 + 2z^3 + 6z^3 = x^2 + 2x^3 - 2y^2 + 2y^5 + 8z^3 =$

$2y^5 + 2x^3 + 8z^3 + x^2 - 2y^2$

Writing the polynomial in standard form:

$2y^5 + 2x^3 + 8z^3 + x^2 - 2y^2 = 2x^3 + x^2 + 2y^5 - 2y^2 + 8z^3$

17) The answer is 550 km

To find the distance traveled in the first 5 hours, add the first 5 numbers.

$40 + 45 + 50 + 35 + 55 = 225$

To find the distance traveled in the next 5 hours, multiply the average by number of hours. $Distance = Average \times Rate = 65 \times 5 = 325$

Add both numbers. $325 + 225 = 550$

The total distance the car traveled in 10 hours is $550 \ km$.

18) The answer is 125%

The question is this: 1.75 is what percent of 1.40? Use percent formula:

$part = percent \times whole, \ 1.75 = x \times 1.40 \Rightarrow percent = \frac{1.75}{1.40} = 125$

1.75 is 125% of 1.40.

19) The answer is 48cm

$One \ liter = 1,000 \ cm^3 \rightarrow 6 \ liters = 6,000 \ cm^3;$

Formula for the volume of a rectangle prism is: $V = l \times w \times h$

$6,000 = 25 \times 5 \times h \rightarrow h = \frac{6,000}{125} = 48 \ cm$

20) The answer is 50

Red and blue balls are in ration of 2:3. Write a proportion and solve.

$\frac{2}{3} = \frac{x}{75} \rightarrow 3x = 2 \times 75 \rightarrow 3x = 150 \rightarrow x = \frac{150}{3} = 50$

21) The answer is 400 *ml*

6% of the volume of the solution is alcohol. Let x be the volume of the solution.

Then: $6\% \ of \ x = 24 \ ml \Rightarrow 0.06 \ x = 24 \Rightarrow x = 24 \div 0.06 = 400$

22) The answer is -4

Solve for x. $\frac{5x}{16} = \frac{x-1}{4}$. Multiply the second fraction by 4. $\frac{5x}{16} = \frac{4(x-1)}{4\times4}$. Two denominators are equal. Therefore, the numerators must be equal.

$5x = 4x - 4 \rightarrow 5x - 4x = -4 \rightarrow x = -4$

23) The answer is $-57 + 7i$

We know that: $i = \sqrt{-1} \Rightarrow i^2 = -1$

Use FOIL (First-Out-In-Last) method:

$(-4 + 9i)(3 + 5i) = -12 - 20i + 27i + 45i^2 = -12 + 7i - 45 = -57 + 7i$

24) The answer is $\frac{12}{13}$

$tan\theta = \frac{opposite}{adjacent}, \ tan\theta = \frac{5}{12} \Rightarrow$ We have the following right triangle. Then:

$c = \sqrt{5^2 + 12^2} = \sqrt{25 + 144} = \sqrt{169} = 13$

$cos\ \theta = \frac{adjacent}{hypotenuse} = \frac{12}{13}$

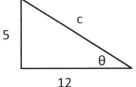

25) The answer is $x = -\frac{4}{3}$

To find the vertical asymptote(s) of a rational function, set the denominator equal to 0 and solve for x. Then: $3x + 4 = 0 \rightarrow 3x = -4 \rightarrow x = -\frac{4}{3}$

The vertical asymptote is $x = -\frac{4}{3}$

26) The answer is 100 miles

Use the information provided in the question to draw the shape.

Use Pythagorean Theorem: $a^2 + b^2 = c^2$

$60^2 + 80^2 = c^2 \Rightarrow 3,600 + 6,400 = c^2 \Rightarrow 10,000 = c^2 \Rightarrow c = 100$

The boat is 100 miles from its starting point.

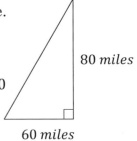

27) The answer is 12

Based on corresponding members from two matrices, we get: $\begin{cases} 2x = x + 3y - 5 \\ 4x = 2y + 10 \end{cases} \rightarrow$

$\begin{cases} x - 3y = -5 \\ 4x - 2y = 10 \end{cases}$, Multiply first equation by -4.

$\begin{cases} -4x + 12y = 20 \\ 4x - 2y = 10 \end{cases} \rightarrow$ add two equations. $10y = 30 \rightarrow y = 3 \rightarrow x = 4 \rightarrow x \times y = 12$

28) The answer is $\frac{9}{20}$

Set of numbers that are not composite between 1 and 20: $A = \{1, 2, 3, 5, 7, 11, 13, 17, 19\}$

$Probability = \dfrac{number\ of\ desired\ outcomes}{number\ of\ total\ outcomes} = \dfrac{9}{20}$

29) The answer is 1

Let's remove each number and calculate the average.

Remove 1. Then: $\quad average = \dfrac{4+5+8+11+12}{5} = \dfrac{40}{5} = 8$

Remove 4. Then: $\quad average = \dfrac{1+5+8+11+12}{5} = \dfrac{37}{5} = 7.4$

Remove 5. Then: $\quad average = \dfrac{1+4+8+11+12}{5} = \dfrac{36}{5} = 7.2$

Remove 8. Then: $\quad average = \dfrac{1+4+5+11+12}{5} = \dfrac{33}{5} = 6.6$

Remove 11. Then: $\quad average = \dfrac{1+4+5+8+12}{5} = \dfrac{30}{5} = 6$

Remove 12. Then: $\quad average = \dfrac{1+4+5+8+11}{5} = \dfrac{29}{5} = 5.8$

Only removing number 1 change the average of the numbers to 8.

30) The answer is 224

$y = 4ab + 3b^3$. Plug in the values of a and b in the equation: $a = 2$ and $b = 4$

$y = 4(2)(4) + 3(4)^3 = 32 + 3(64) = 32 + 192 = 224$

31) The answer is 61

The sum of two supplementary angles is 180 degrees. Then: $(2x - 6) + (x + 3) = 180$

Simplify and solve for x: $(2x - 6) + (x + 3) = 180 \rightarrow 3x - 3 = 180 \rightarrow 3x = 180 + 3 \rightarrow 3x = 183 \rightarrow x = 61$

32) The answer is "*no solution*"

When the logarithms have the same base: $f(x) = g(y)$, then: $x = y$,
$log(5x + 2) = log(3x - 1) \rightarrow 5x + 2 = 3x - 1 \rightarrow$

$5x + 2 - 3x + 1 = 0 \rightarrow 2x + 3 = 0 \rightarrow 2x = -3 \rightarrow x = -\frac{3}{2}$

Verify Solution: $log(5x + 2) = log\left(5\left(-\frac{3}{2}\right) + 2\right) = log(-5.5)$

Logarithms of negative numbers are not defined. Therefore, there is no solution for this equation.

33) The answer is $x = \frac{b+8}{a-1}$

To solve for x bring all terms that contain x. Subtract x from both sides:
$$ax - 8 - x = x + b - x \rightarrow ax - x - 8 = b$$
Add 8 to both sides: $ax - x - 8 + 8 = b + 8 \rightarrow ax - x = b + 8$

Factorize $ax - x$. Then: $ax - x = b + 8 \rightarrow x(a - 1) = b + 8$

Now, divide both sides by $(a - 1)$: $\frac{x(a-1)}{(a-1)} = \frac{b+8}{(a-1)} \rightarrow x = \frac{b+8}{a-1}$

34) The answer is $(\infty, -3] \cup [5, \infty)$

First solve: $x^2 - 2x - 15 = 0$, Factor: $x^2 - 2x - 15 = 0 \rightarrow (x - 5)(x + 3) = 0$.

-3 and 5 are the solutions. Choose a point between -3 and 5. Let's choose 0.

Then: $x = 0 \rightarrow x^2 - 2x - 15 \geq 0 \rightarrow (0)^2 - 2(0) - 15 \geq 0 \rightarrow -15 \geq 0$.

This is NOT true. So, the solution is: $x \leq -3$ or $x \geq 5$. The solution is shown on the following number line.

Using interval notation, the solution is: $(\infty, -3] \cup [5, \infty)$

35) The answer is (Domain: $x \geq -2$, Range: $f(x) \geq 8$)

For domain: Find non-negative values for radicals: $2x + 4 \geq 0$

Domain of functions: $2x + 4 \geq 0 \rightarrow 2x \geq -4 \rightarrow x \geq -2$

Domain of the function $y = 3\sqrt{2x + 4} + 8$: $x \geq -2$

For range: The range of a radical function of the form $c\sqrt{ax + b} + k$ is: $f(x) \geq k$

For the function $y = 3\sqrt{2x + 4} + 8$, the value of k is 8. Then: $f(x) \geq 8$

Range of the function $y = 3\sqrt{2x + 4} + 8$: $f(x) \geq 8$

ALEKS Mathematics Practice Test 2 Answers and Explanations

1) The answer is $\frac{7y+7}{18}$

To solve for x, isolate it on one side of the equation. Add $7y$ to both sides:

$7 = 18x - 7y \rightarrow 7y + 7 = 18x - 7y + 7y \rightarrow 7y + 7 = 18x$. Now, divide both sides by 18: $\frac{7y+7}{18} = \frac{18x}{18} \rightarrow x = \frac{7y+7}{18}$

2) The answer is 2.5

Use distance formula: $Distance = Rate \times time$

We can write this equation for the distance traveled by the two trains:

$r_1t + r_2t = d$, by substituting the speed (rate) of each train, we have:

$90t + 80t = 425$, now solve for t (time). Then: $170t = 425 \rightarrow \frac{170t}{170} = \frac{425}{170} \rightarrow t = 2.5$

After 2.5 hours (two hours and thirty minutes) the two trains will be exactly 425 miles apart.

3) The answer is $x > 1$

To simplify this inequality, we need to isolate the variable on one side of the inequality. Add -6 to both sides. $-6 + 2x > -4 \rightarrow -6 + 2x + 6 > -4 + 6 \rightarrow$

$2x > 2 \rightarrow \frac{2x}{2} > \frac{2}{2} \rightarrow x > 1$

4) The answer is $(4, 3)$

To solve this system of equation, add the two equations. Then:

$\begin{cases} x + 2y = 10 \\ 6x - 2y = 18 \end{cases} \rightarrow x + 6x + 2y - 2y = 10 + 18 \rightarrow 7x = 28 \rightarrow x = 4$

Substitute the value of x in the second equation and solve for y:

$x + 2y = 10, x = 4 \rightarrow 4 + 2y = 10 \rightarrow 2y = 10 - 4 \rightarrow 2y = 6 \rightarrow y = 3$

5) The answer is $-\frac{4}{5}$

Use the slope equation: $m = \frac{y_2 - y_1}{x_2 - x_1} \rightarrow \frac{7-3}{-9+4} = \frac{4}{-5} \rightarrow m = -\frac{4}{5}$

The slope of the line is $-\frac{4}{5}$.

6) The answer is $4x$

To find the $\left(\frac{f}{g}\right)(x)$, divide $f(x)$ by $g(x)$. $f(x) = -8x^2 + 12x$ and $g(x) = -2x + 3$.

Then: $\left(\frac{f}{g}\right)(x) = \frac{f(x)}{g(x)} = \frac{-8x^2 + 12x}{-2x + 3}$

Factor the numerator $(-8x^2 + 12x)$. Take the common factor $4x$ out:

$-8x^2 + 12x = 4x(-2x + 3) \rightarrow \dfrac{-8x^2 + 12x}{-2x + 3} = \dfrac{4x(-2x + 3)}{-2x + 3}$

Cancel out the common factor $(-2x + 3)$: $\frac{4x(-2x+3)}{-2x+3} = 4x$

7) The answer is $\$1,080$

Use simple interest formula:

$I = prt$ (I = interest, p = principal, r = rate, t = time)

$I = (12,000)(0.045)(2) = 1,080$

If you deposit $\$12,000$ in the bank, you will earn $\$1,080$ interest in two years.

8) The answer is $9,600$

Number of visiting fans: $\frac{2 \times 24,000}{5} = 9,600$ (notice that the ratio of visiting fans to total seats is 2 to 5)

9) The answer is $120°$

The sum of all angles in a quadrilateral is 360 degrees. Let x be the smallest angle in the quadrilateral. Then the angles are: $2x, 3x, 3x, 4x, 2x + 3x + 3x + 4x = 360 \rightarrow 12x = 360 \rightarrow x = 30$

The angles in the quadrilateral are: $60°, 90°, 90°,$ and $120°$.

10) The answer is $\frac{7\sqrt{\pi}}{\pi}$

Formula for the area of a circle is: $A = \pi r^2$. Using 49 for the area of the circle we have: $49 = \pi r^2$. Let's solve for the radius (r).

$$\frac{49}{\pi} = r^2 \rightarrow r = \sqrt{\frac{49}{\pi}} = \frac{7}{\sqrt{\pi}} = \frac{7}{\sqrt{\pi}} \times \frac{\sqrt{\pi}}{\sqrt{\pi}} = \frac{7\sqrt{\pi}}{\pi}$$

11) The answer is $90cm$

Length of the rectangle is: $\frac{5}{4} \times 20 = 25cm$, perimeter of rectangle is:

$2 \times (length + width) = 2 \times (20 + 25) = 90cm$

12) The answer is $135°$

The angle x and 45 are supplementary angles. Therefore: $x + 45 = 180 \rightarrow$

$x = 180° - 45° = 135°$

13) The answer is $18°$

The sum of supplement angles is 180. Let x be that angle.

Therefore, $x + 9x = 180$, $10x = 180$, divide both sides by 10: $x = 18$

The measure of the angle is 18 degrees.

14) The answer is $x = \frac{3}{2}$

Use the cross multiplication to solve for x:

$\frac{5}{x+1} = \frac{x+1}{x^2-1} \rightarrow 5(x^2 - 1) = (x + 1)(x + 1)$

Simplify $5(x^2 - 1)$ using the distributive property: $5(x^2 - 1) = 5x^2 - 5$

Simplify $(x + 1)(x + 1)$ using the FOIL (First-Out-In-Last) method:

$(x + 1)(x + 1) = x^2 + x + x + 1 = x^2 + 2x + 1$

Then: $5(x^2 - 1) = (x + 1)(x + 1) \rightarrow 5x^2 - 5 = x^2 + 2x + 1$. Since this is a quadratic equation, we need to bring all terms to one side of the equation. Subtract $(x^2 + 2x + 1)$ from both sides. Then:

$5x^2 - 5 - (x^2 + 2x + 1) = x^2 + 2x + 1 - (x^2 + 2x + 1)$

Simplify and combine like terms: $5x^2 - 5 - x^2 - 2x - 1$

$= x^2 + 2x + 1 - (x^2 + 2x + 1) \rightarrow 4x^2 - 2x - 6 = 0$

Use the quadratic formula to solve for x. Then: $x_{1,2} = \frac{-b \pm \sqrt{b^2 - 4ac}}{2a} =$

$\frac{-(-2) \pm \sqrt{(-2)^2 - 4(4)(-6)}}{2(4)} = \frac{-(-2) \pm \sqrt{100}}{8} \rightarrow x = \frac{-(-2) + 10}{8} = \frac{2 + 10}{8} = \frac{12}{8} = \frac{3}{2}$ or $x = \frac{-(-2) - 10}{8} =$

$\frac{2 - 10}{8} = \frac{-8}{8} = -1$

The solution $x = -1$ is not defined in the original equation. (If $x = -1$, then the denominators equal to zero, which is not defined.) Therefore, the solution $x = \frac{3}{2}$ is the only accepted solution.

15) The answer is 62,500

Three times of 25,000 is 75,000. One sixth of them cancelled their tickets. One sixth of 75,000 equals 12,500 ($\frac{1}{6} \times 72,000 = 12,500$). 62,500 ($72,000 - 12,000 = 62,500$) fans are attending this week.

16) The answer is $\frac{\sqrt{8}}{3}$

$sin A = \frac{1}{3} \Rightarrow$ Since $sin\theta = \frac{opposite}{hypotenuse}$,

we have the following right triangle. Then:

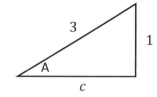

$c = \sqrt{3^2 - 1^2} = \sqrt{9-1} = \sqrt{8}$, $Cos\ \theta = \frac{adjacent}{hypotenuse} \Rightarrow cos A = \frac{\sqrt{8}}{3}$

17) The answer is 25π

The equation of a circle in standard form is: $(x - h)^2 + (y - k)^2 = r^2$, where r is the radius of the circle. In this circle, the radius is 5. $r^2 = 25 \rightarrow r = 5$, $(x + 2)^2 + (y - 4)^2 = 25$

Area of a circle: $A = \pi r^2 = \pi(5)^2 = 25\pi$

18) The answer is 5.8×10^5

In scientific notation all numbers are written in the form of: $m \times 10^n$, where m is between 1 and 10. To find an equivalent value of 580,000, write a decimal point after 5 which is a number between 1 and 10. Then: 5.80000

Now, determine how many decimal digits we have on the right side of the decimal point. Then put it as the power of 10. There are 5 digits on the right side of the decimal point. Then:

$580,000 = 5.8 \times 10^5$

19) The answer is 200

The ratio of boy to girls is $2:3$. Therefore, there are 2 boys out of 5 students. To find the answer, first divide the total number of students by 5, then multiply the result by two. $500 \div 5 = 100 \Rightarrow 100 \times 2 = 200$. There are 200 boys in the school.

20) The answer is 40

First, find the number. Let x be the number. Write the equation and solve for x.

150% of a number is 75, then: $1.5 \times x = 75 \Rightarrow x = \frac{75}{1.5} = 50$

80% of 50 is: $0.8 \times 50 = 40$

21) The answer is $c(3, -2)$, radius = 3

The standard form of circle equation is: $(x - h)^2 + (y - k)^2 = r^2$ where the radius of the circle is r, and it's centered at (h, k).

First, move the loose number to the right side: $x^2 + y^2 - 6x + 4y = -4$

Group x-variables and y-variables together: $(x^2 - 6x) + (y^2 + 4y) = -4$

Convert x to square form:

$(x^2 - 6x + 9) + y^2 - 6y = -4 + 9 \rightarrow (x - 3)^2 + (y^2 + 4y) = -4 + 9$

Convert y to square form:

$(x - 3)^2 + (y^2 + 4y + 4) = -4 + 9 + 4 \rightarrow (x - 3)^2 + (y + 2)^2 = 9$

Then, the equation of the circle in standard form is: $(x - 3)^2 + (y + 2)^2 = 3^2$

The center of the circle is at $(3, -2)$ and its radius is 3.

22) The answer is $x \leq -2 \cup x \geq 6$

Since this inequality contains absolute value, then, the value inside absolute value bars is greater than -4 and less than 4. Then:

$x - 2 \geq 4 \rightarrow x \geq 4 + 2 \rightarrow x \geq 6$, or $x - 2 \leq -4 \rightarrow x \leq -4 + 2 \rightarrow x \leq -2$

The solution is: $x \leq -2 \cup x \geq 6$

23) The answer is $\dfrac{8}{17}$

$tan\theta = \dfrac{opposite}{adjacent}$, and $tan\, x = \dfrac{8}{15}$, therefore, the opposite side of the angle x is 8 and the adjacent side is 15. Let's draw the triangle.

Using Pythagorean theorem, we have:

$a^2 + b^2 = c^2 \rightarrow 8^2 + 15^2 = c^2 \rightarrow 64 + 225 = c^2 \rightarrow c = 17,$

$sin\, x = \dfrac{opposite}{hypotenuse} = \dfrac{8}{17}$

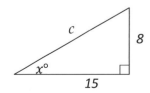

24) The answer is $x^{\frac{21}{4}}$

Use Exponent's rules: $(x^a)^b = x^{a \times b}$. Then: $(x^6)^{\frac{7}{8}} = x^{6 \times \frac{7}{8}} = x^{\frac{42}{8}} = x^{\frac{21}{4}}$

25) The answers are $0, -2, -3$

Frist factor the function: $f(x) = x^3 + 5x^2 + 6x = x(x+2)(x+3)$

To find the zeros, $f(x)$ should be zero. $f(x) = x(x+2)(x+3) = 0$, Therefore, the zeros are: $x = 0$, $(x+2) = 0 \Rightarrow x = -2$, $(x+3) = 0 \Rightarrow x = -3$

26) The answer is 2

We know that: $sin^2 a + cos^2 a = 1$

Then: $x + sin^2 a + cos^2 a = 3 \rightarrow x + 1 = 3 \rightarrow x = 2$

27) The answer is $\frac{y}{5}$

Solve for x. $\sqrt{5x} = \sqrt{y}$.

Square both sides of the equation: $\left(\sqrt{5x}\right)^2 = \left(\sqrt{y}\right)^2 \rightarrow 5x = y \rightarrow x = \frac{y}{5}$

28) The answer is 59.48

$average = \frac{sum\ of\ terms}{number\ of\ terms}$, the sum of the weight of all girls is: $18 \times 55 = 990\ kg$

The sum of the weight of all boys is: $32 \times 62 = 1,984\ kg$. The sum of the weight of all students is: $990 + 1,984 = 2,974\ kg$. $average = \frac{2,974}{50} = 59.48$

29) The answer is 46

Plug in the value of x and y. $x = 3$ and $y = -3$

$5(x - 2y) + (2 - x)^2 = 5\big(3 - 2(-3)\big) + (2 - 3)^2$

$= 5(3 + 6) + (-1)^2 = 45 + 1 = 46$

30) The answer is on the following graph

A quadratic function in vertex form is: $y = a(x - h)^2 + k$ and (h, k) is the vertex.

Then, the vertex of $y = (x + 1)^2 - 2$ is $(-1, -2)$.

Substitute zero for x and solve for y: $y = (0 + 1)^2 - 2 = -1$.

The y Intercept is $(0, -1)$. Now, you can simply graph the quadratic function. Notice that quadratic function is a U-shaped curve. (you can plug in some values of x and solve for y to get some points on the graph.)

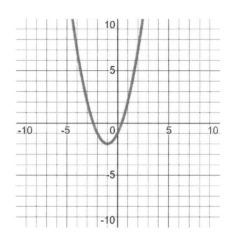

31) The answer is $7a - 49$

First, use distribute property to simplify $4(a - 7)$ and $5(a + 3)$.

$4(a - 7) = 4a - 28$ and $5(a + 3) = 5a + 15$. Then:

$8a - 6 + 4(a - 7) - 5(a + 3) = 8a - 6 + 4a - 28 - 5a - 15 = 7a - 49$

32) The answer is 61

Plug in the value of x and y in the expression. $x = 3$ and $y = 7$

$6x^2 - 2xy + y^2 = 6(3)^2 - 2(3)(7) + (7)^2 = 6(9) - 42 + 49 \rightarrow 54 - 42 + 49 = 61$

33) The answer is 105

$P = 120 \rightarrow S = 0.7(120) + 21 = 105$

34) The answer is 10

Use fractions division rule: $\frac{a}{b} \div \frac{c}{d} = \frac{a}{b} \times \frac{d}{c} = \frac{a \times d}{b \times c}$

Then: $\frac{5x}{x+3} \div \frac{x}{2x+6} = \frac{5x}{x+3} \times \frac{2x+6}{x} = \frac{5x(2x+6)}{x(x+3)} = \frac{5x \times 2(x+3)}{x(x+3)}$

Cancel common factor: $\frac{5x \times 2(x+3)}{x(x+3)} = \frac{10x(x+3)}{x(x+3)} = 10$

35) The answer is $x = \frac{ln(12)}{2}$

If $f(x) = g(x), then: ln(f(x)) = ln(g(x)) \rightarrow ln(e^{2x}) = ln(12)$

Use logarithm rule: $log_a x^b = b \, log_a x \rightarrow ln(e^{2x}) = 2x \, ln(e) \rightarrow (2x)ln(e) = ln(12)$

$ln(e) = 1$, then: $(2x)ln(e) = ln(12) \rightarrow 2x = ln(12) \rightarrow x = \frac{ln(12)}{2}$

... So Much More Online!

Effortless Math Online ALEKS Math Center offers a complete study program, including the following:

- ✓ Step-by-step instructions on how to prepare for the ALEKS Math test

- ✓ Numerous ALEKS Math worksheets to help you measure your math skills

- ✓ Complete list of ALEKS Math formulas

- ✓ Video lessons for ALEKS Math topics

- ✓ Full-length ALEKS Math practice tests

- ✓ And much more...

No Registration Required.

Visit **EffortlessMath.com/ALEKS** to find your online ALEKS Math resources.

Receive the PDF version of this book or get another FREE book!

Thank you for using our Book!

Do you LOVE this book?

Then, you can get the PDF version of this book or another book absolutely FREE!

Please email us at:

info@EffortlessMath.com

for details.

Author's Final Note

I hope you enjoyed reading this book. You've made it through the book! Great job!

First of all, thank you for purchasing this study guide. I know you could have picked any number of books to help you prepare for your ALEKS Math test, but you picked this book and for that I am extremely grateful.

It took me years to write this study guide for the ALEKS Math because I wanted to prepare a comprehensive ALEKS Math study guide to help test takers make the most effective use of their valuable time while preparing for the test.

After teaching and tutoring math courses for over a decade, I've gathered my personal notes and lessons to develop this study guide. It is my greatest hope that the lessons in this book could help you prepare for your test successfully.

If you have any questions, please contact me at reza@effortlessmath.com and I will be glad to assist. Your feedback will help me to greatly improve the quality of my books in the future and make this book even better. Furthermore, I expect that I have made a few minor errors somewhere in this study guide. If you think this to be the case, please let me know so I can fix the issue as soon as possible.

If you enjoyed this book and found some benefit in reading this, I'd like to hear from you and hope that you could take a quick minute to post a review on the book's Amazon page. To leave your valuable feedback, please visit: amzn.to/3tlvmCZ

Or scan this QR code.

I personally go over every single review, to make sure my books really are reaching out and helping students and test takers. Please help me help ALEKS Math test takers, by leaving a review!

I wish you all the best in your future success!

Reza Nazari

Math teacher and author

Made in the USA
Monee, IL
14 March 2022

92870660R10153